Railway Track Diagrams

Book 3
Western

Managing Editor
Mike Bridge

Railway Track Diagrams

Book 3: Western

Contents

1st Edition 1989
2nd Edition 1992
3rd Edition 2000
4th Edition 2005

ISBN 978-0-9549866-6-7

© TRACKmaps 2010

Published by Trackmaps, Little Court, Upper South Wraxall, Bradford on Avon BA15 2SE
Web: www.trackmaps.co.uk

Produced by ESR Cartography Ltd, Woodley, Reading RG5 3LE
Cover design by Pastiche Art Studio, Swindon SN6 8TZ
Cover Photos © RailImages, Leigh-on-Sea SS9 4AL
Printed by Brightsea Press, Exeter EX5 2UL

Managing Editor: Mike Bridge
Digital Cartography: David Padgett
Developed from the original cartography of John Yonge

Publisher's Note
Every effort has been made by the editor to ensure the accuracy of the information in the book is as correct as possible at the time of going to press. Notwithstanding, the Publishers welcome corrections, updates or suggestions for application to future editions

Railway Track Diagrams
Book 3: Western

Preface to the Track Diagram Series

Quail Track Diagrams have been published since 1988 and provide a reference to Enthusiasts and Industry alike. They contain information which may exist elsewhere and in other forms but are unique in making it all available in one easily portable volume.

Originally published by the Quail Map Co, edited by Gerald Jacobs with cartography by John Yonge, the series covers the entire UK mainland network and includes freight lines, light rail, heritage railways, private railways and Transport for London. The information included is a combination of historical sources collected by Gerald Jacobs during his 40 years with British Railways, subsequently kept up to date with reference to Network Rail and its predecessors and supplemented by other data, by the kind assistance of other persons and by field observation. In 2004, Trackmaps took over the publication of these volumes and embarked on the digital conversion of the information into the form seen here. The Railway Track Diagrams have become a popular work for railway enthusiasts and a de-facto standard in the rail industry.

However, records are wonderful things. They can both inform and confuse. Nowhere is this more certain than on the UK Railway Network. Built up, as it has been, over more than 180 years, managed as individual companies, as a nationalised industry and now as individual train operating companies with a single infrastructure owner, it has grown, stagnated, declined and grown again more than once within that time. Many people have produced records and maps at different times for different areas, both within the industry and outside. Many record systems complement each other while others conflict. Track Diagrams attempt to collate these diverse sources into one publication but, even so, space precludes the inclusion of much detail including, for example, signals.

Track Diagrams also try to put down a standard where discrepancies occur; mileages are typical. Mileages often vary slightly between different official records but, in general, those given in Sectional Appendix have been used. Station mileages are usually taken from the mid-point of the platforms or, in the case of a terminus, the buffer stops. The Railway is continually changing and, because of its diverse nature and varied history, discrepancies often arise between seeming accurate sources. In such circumstances, the Editor's judgment is applied.

Trackmaps, August 2010

Introduction

The Track Diagrams in this book cover most of the lines forming the Western Route of Network Rail, together with a small part of LNW and Wessex Routes and a number of private railways and industrial layouts. They are, in general, up to date as at August 2010. Some works already started but not yet finished have been included, such as the Cotswold re-doubling and an additional inset has been included for works at Reading up to 2011. The final layouts of that project are far enough ahead to be held for the next edition. One major feature throughout the region has been the steady lifting of siding complexes and the closure of private terminals with only the opening of Bristol Freightliner Railport and Birdport to compensate.

This 5th Edition has a number of differences to its predecessor. In the last edition, multiple types of asset at any particular location were grouped under a single name in the Location Index. The Index has now been extended to name each item separately. There are still some items, such as barrow and footpath crossings which have been left out, but overall the Index has grown by 25%. The ELR Index now benefits from starting and finishing map references and an LOR Index has been added, with map references, to reflect the common use these codes now have in the rail industry.

There has been some re-configuration of the maps but the most significant change has been the exclusion of leisure and miniature railways. There are now over 490 minor railways in the UK with a constant flux and these are well served by other publications to the extent that the selection of just a few for inclusion here seems completely arbitrary. As a consequence, Track Diagrams will now limit the inclusion of non-pubic service railways to standard gauge heritage lines, either attached to or previously part of the national network, or narrow gauge lines with a heritage of their own.

Acknowledgements

A tremendous amount of work goes into the Railway Track Diagram Series. Although much information is available from official sources, it still has to be assessed, varied in some cases and prepared before the cartographer can do his job. Many details off the beaten path and on private lines have to be teased out from elsewhere. For this edition, the Managing Editor has been extremely grateful for the significant input of Myles Munsey, Gerald Jacobs, Nigel Farebrother and Roland Pittard, together with contributions from Ross Muggeridge, Stephen Phillips, Richard Atkinson, Stephen Hegginbotham, Ralph Windeatt, Paul Conibeare, Shaun Hodges, Ivor Dixon, Ian Newbold and Bob Gorringe. Peter Scott, the publisher of "Minor Railways" (now in its 22nd edition) and creator of Minor Railways Online (http://web.ukonline.co.uk/pe.scott/), has been very kind in providing information for several of the Heritage lines and other assistance came from Phil Deaves, Gordon Edwards, Paul Higgins, Mick Donovan and Nick Whitfield. Other acknowledgements are due to the Branch Line Society and the Railway Correspondence and Travel Society. The Managing Editor would also like to give special thanks for the forbearance of cartographer Dave Padgett at ESR Cartography Ltd through the trials and tribulations of getting from scribbles to print. To every one of the helpers, with significant input or with small, your efforts are greatly appreciated.

Mike Bridge, Managing Editor, August 2010

KEY

————————	Running Line
————————	Siding
————————	Electrified overhead
————————	Electrified 3rd rail
————————	Electrified 3rd rail (Underail contact, DLR)
————————	Electrified 4th rail (LU)
————————	Electrified, overhead & Conductor rail
··················	Proposed or under construction.
——●——	Line obstructed
——○-- -	Line 'in situ' but out of use, partly dismantled, buried, or overgrown
——·——	Change of Signalling mandate
W ╫ LNW	Network Rail Territory boundary
Bristol ┃ Swindon (B) ┃ (SN)	Signal Box / centre area limits (Within an area, plates on automatic signals may reflect actual line description)
—)---(—	Tunnel
——⌣——	Bridge under Rail or Viaduct
——Y——	Selected Motorway / Trunk Road bridges over rail
——+——	Network Rail operated level crossing
——¦——	User-worked crossing with Telephone
←——→	Track signalled in both directions (a double arrow indicates normal direction of travel) (On single lines 'DN' indicates down direction)
——⋈——	Private siding boundary, often marked by a gate
⌐———	Sand Drag / Trap Point
——◯—ᴬ—▢	Turntable / Friction Arrester
——‡——	Gantry Rails (Freightliner Terminal)
—×—×—×—	Fence
wwwwwwwww	Wall / Bank
——▲——	Hot Axle Box Detector (HABD), Wheel Impact Load Detector (WILD) or Wheelchex Device

MLN	ELR-Engineer's Line Reference (Prefix and suffix numbers indicate sub-divisions and their boundaries)
[GW 103]	Line of Route Code
¦ 93	Whole mileposts, shown on the appropriate side of the line
¦ 32	Whole kilometre posts
81.3	End of mileage run
113.76 / 105.70 COM	Lineside mileage change
▇3	Platform with number (May be supplemented by sub-divisions. e.g. (a), (b), (c), 'N' or North etc)
⑦	Indicates number of carriages per platform (approx 20m lengths)
⸬	Provisional proposed platform
☐	Former Royal Mail platform
☐	Platform out of use
⌐┘	Other feature (labelled)
▨	Loading bank / dock
Exeter (E) ⊠	Signal Box or Signalling Centre, with code (underlined text relates to SB or SC)
◩	Control Panel
⬛	Gate Box
□· ⊙	Ground Frame/Ground Switch Panel or Shunting Frame. ⑤ Indicates 'Shut in' facility
⊛	Radio electronic token block / Token exchange point
¶	Proposed closure
◯	Water tower
∧	Summit, height in feet
(Marazion) ●	Indicates a former Jn, Station or Signal Box
86.34 (Not italic if Station mileage)	Distance in Miles and chains from specified zero 1 Mile = 1760 yards / 1.6km 80 chains = 1 Mile 1 chain = 22 yards / 20.11m
57.60 km	Distance in Kilometres

London Underground Signalling

LU signalling is controlled at some places by local Signal Cabins, or for a long part or the whole of some lines by Signal Control Centres.
Because of different cables, LU has Interlocking Machines operated by air motors (or comparable equipment) in unmanned rooms near points, except where a local cabin has an interlocking lever frame.
IMR's (and equivalent rooms) are included in these maps, but purely Relay Rooms (and their equivalents) are not.
IMR's bear the name of the adjacent station unless otherwise noted: (e) indicates location at the end of the platform, (m) in the middle of the platform

ⓙⓙ	Unmanned Interlocking Machine (or comparable equipment) Room, with code	ⓙⓟ	Interlocking within manned cabin, with code(s), controlled
ⓦⓟ	Interlocking inside former cabin, with code	JP ¦ JJ	Code area boundaries (where not separated by a long stretch of plain track(s))

Guide references are given to pre-nationalisation, pre-grouping and sometimes pioneer railways e.g. GW : Wilts, Somerset & Weymouth

Traditional Line Descriptions may be quoted, e.g. **SOUTH WALES AND BRISTOL DIRECT LINE**

GENERAL ABBREVIATIONS

AA	Acid Application	FP	Fuelling Point or Footpath	PW	Permanent Way
ABP	Associated British Ports	ft	Feet	Qy	Query concerning distances etc, unresolved
AC	Alternating Current	GB	Gate Box	REC	Reception
ARR	Arrival	GC	Gantry Crane	RETB	Radio Electronic Token Block
ASC	Area Signalling Centre i/c IECC, Power Box	GDS	Goods	REV	Reversing or Reversible line
bdy	boundary	GF	Ground Frame	RR	Run-Round
BCH	Branch	GL	Goods Loop	S	South
BR	British Rail	GS	Goods Shed	S & T	Signal & Telegraph
CCTV	Closed Circuit Television	GSP	Ground Switch Panel	SB	Signal Box or Southbound
CET	Controlled Emission Toilet Discharge	H	Headshunt	SC	Signalling Centre
CL	Crossing Loop on Single Line	HABD	Hot Axle Box Detector	SCC	Signalling Control Centre
COM	Change of Mileage	HH	Hopper House	Sdg(s)	Siding(s)
CR	Cripple Siding	HST	High Speed Train	SD	Sand Drag
CW	Carriage Washer	IECC	Intergrated Electronic Control Centre	SF	Shunting Frame
C&W	Carriage & Wagon	Jn	Junction	SIMBIDS	Simplified Bi-Directional Signalling
D	Connections Disconnected	Jt	Joint	SN	Shunt Neck
DA	Down Avoiding	km	kilometres	SP	Switch Panel
DBS	DB Schenker Rail (UK) Ltd	L	Wheel Lathe	SS	Shunt Spur
DC	Direct Current	LC	Level Crossing (manned, automatic or open)	TA	Tamper siding
DE	Down Electric	LHS	Locomotive Holding Siding	TB	Turnback Siding
DED	Diesel Electric Depot	LP	Loop	TEP	Token Exchange Point
DEP	Departure	LPG	Liquified petroleum gas	TL	Traffic Lights
DF	Down Fast	LS	Locomotive Shed	TMD	Traction Maintenance Depot
DG	Down Goods	LW	Locomotive Washer	T&RSMD	Traction & Rolling Stock Maintenance Depot
DGL	Down Goods Loop	M	Middle	U&D	Up & Down
DL	Down Loop	M ch	Miles and Chains	UA	Up Avoiding
DM	Down Main	M&EE	Mechanical & Electrical Engineer	UE	Up Electric
DMD	Diesel Maintenance Depot	MGR	'Merry-go-round'	UF	Up Fast
DMUD	Diesel Multiple Unit Depot	MN	Main	UFN	Until Further Notice
DN	Down	MOD	Ministry of Defence	UG	Up Goods
DPL	Down Passenger Loop	MU	Maintenance Unit	UGL	Up Goods Loop
DR	Down Relief	N	North	UH	Unloading Hopper
DRS	Down Refuge Sidings	n	not electrified	UL	Up Loop
DS	Down Slow	NB	Northbound	UM	Up Main
DSB	Down Surburban	NIRU	Not in regular use	UPL	Up Passenger Loop
DT	Down Through	NR	Network Rail	UR	Up Relief
E	East	OHC	Overhead Crane	URS	Up Refuge Siding
e	elecrified	OHLE	Overhead Line Equipment	US	Up Slow
EB	Eastbound	OOU	Out of Use	USB	Up Suburban
EGF	Emergency Ground Frame	ONS	Overhead Neutral Section	UT	Up Through
EMD	Electric Maintenance Depot	OTM	On-track Maintenance	V or Vdct	Viaduct
EMUD	Electric Multiple Unit Depot	P	Points padlocked	W	West
Engrs	Engineers' Sidings	PAD	Prefabricated Assembly Depot	WB	Westbound or Weighbridge
eol	End of Line	PL	Passenger Loop	WD	War Department or Wheelchex Device
ESP	Emergency Signalling Panel	PS	Private Siding	WILD	Wheel Impact Load Detector
FA	Flushing Apron	PSB	Power Signal Box	yds	yards

SUPPLEMENTARY ABBREVIATIONS FOR THIS BOOK

AD&R	former Alexandra Dock & Railway	LUL	London Underground Limited
B&M	former Brecon & Merthyr Railway	Met	former Metropolitan Railway
BP&G	former Burry Port & Gwendraeth Valley Railway	Mid	former Midland Railway
CTRL	Channel Tunnel Rail Link	MSW	former Midland & South Western Jn Railway
FGW	First Great Western	N&B	former Neath & Brecon Railway
GC	former Great Central Railway	NL	former North London Railway
GW	former Great Western Railway	N&SWJn	former North and South Western Jn Railway
H&C	former Hammersmith & City Joint Line	R&SB	former Rhondda & Swansea Bay Railway
LBSC	former London, Brighton and South Coast Railway	S	former Southern Railway
LCD	former London, Chatham and Dover Railway	S&D	former Somerset & Dorset Railway
LMS	former London Midland and Scottish Railway	SE	former South Eastern Railway
LNE	former London and North Eastern Railway	SWT	South West Trains
LNW	former London and North Western Railway	TV	former Taff Vale Railway
LPTB	former London Passenger Transport Board	WL	former West London Joint Railway
LSW	former London and South Western Railway	WLE	former West London Extension Joint Railway

LEVEL CROSSING ABBREVIATIONS

STANDARD	Supplementary	Description	STANDARD	Supplementary	Description
(ABCL) *		Automatic Barrier Crossing, Locally monitored		(MWLO)	Miniature Warning Lights at Open crossing
(AHBC) *		Automatic Half-Barrier Crossing	(OC)	(O) (OPEN)	Open Crossing (non-automatic), without barriers, gates or road traffic signals
(AOCL) *		Automatic Open Crossing, Locally monitored			
	(AOCR)	Automatic Open Crossing, Remotely monitored	(RC)		Remotely Controlled crossing with barriers
	(BW)	Bridle Way	(R/G)		User-worked crossing with Red and Green warning lights operated by approaching trains
(CCTV)		Manually controlled barrier crossing with Closed Circuit Television			
			(TMO)		Traincrew Operated crossing
	(FP (B)(G)(K)(W))	Footpath crossing (only shown if telephone provided)		(TMOB)	Traincrew Operated Barrier
		(B) Barriers, (G) Gates, (K) Kissing Gate, (W) Wickets		(TMOG)	Traincrew Operated Gates
(MCB)	(MB)	Manually controlled Crossing with Barriers	(UWC)	(UWCP)	User-Worked Crossing of occupation, accommodation or bridleway status with telephone
	(MCBR)	Manually controlled Crossing with Barriers, Remotely controlled			
(MG)	(MCG)	Manually controlled Crossing with Gates		(UWB)	User-Worked Barriers
	(MGH)	Manned Gates, Hand worked		(UWCM)	User-Worked Crossing with miniature Red and Green warning lights
	(MGW)	Manned Gates with Wickets			
	(MSL (B)(F)(G))	Miniature Stop Light with (B) Barriers, (F) Footpath, (G) Gates		(UWG)	User-Worked Gates
	(MWL)	Miniature Warning Lights		(UWK)	User-Worked with Kissing Gates
	(MWLB)	Miniature Warning Lights with Barriers		(UWS)	User-Worked Stile
	(MWLF)	Miniature Warning Lights at user-worked Footpath		(UWW)	User-Worked Wickets
	(MWLG)	Miniature Warning Lights with Gates		(WL)	Barrow or Foot Crossing with White Light indicators

(-X) shown after these abbreviations e.g. (AHBC-X) indicates that the crossing works automatically for movements in the wrong direction.

In some cases, the code of the controlling signal box may be shown e.g. (AHBC-X) (KS).

If no abbreviation is shown, the level crossing is either operated locally by a Signaller or Crossing Keeper, or privately but equipped with a telephone.

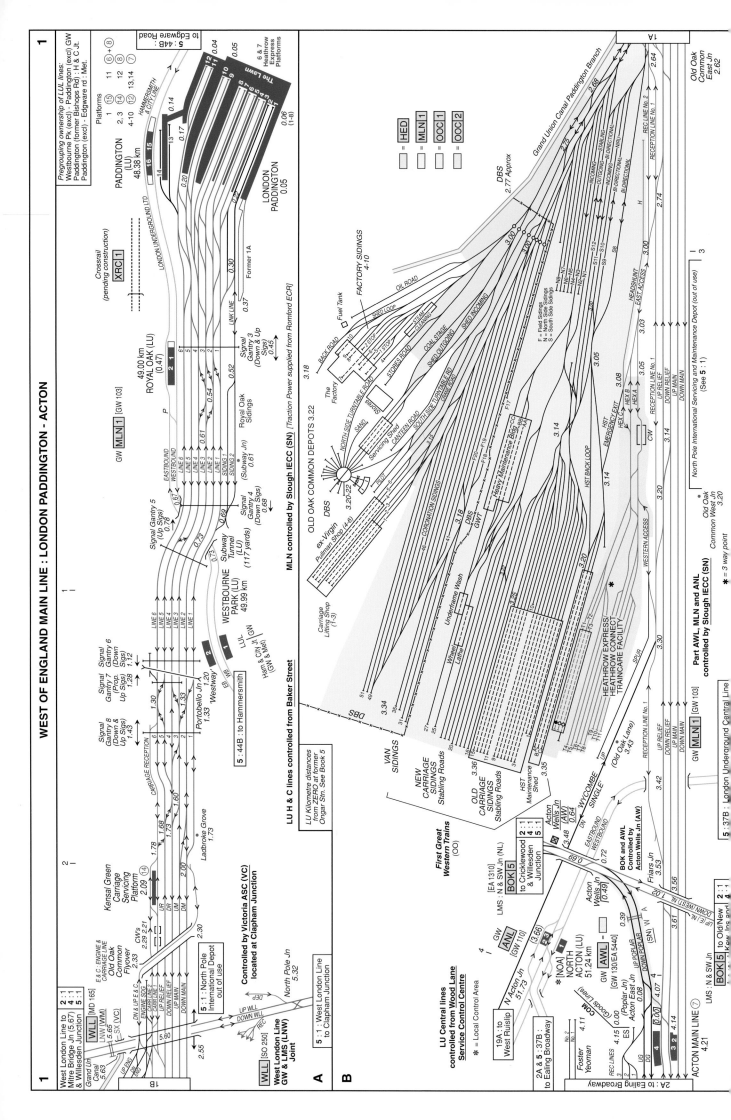

2

August 2010

A

1B : to Paddington

ACTON RAIL TERMINAL
DBS

Engineers' Materials
Handling Sidings

Yeoman
Aggregates

HH

Loco
Stabling
Roads

4.31

4.43   RECEPTION No. 3
        RECEPTION No. 2
        RECEPTION No. 1

DOWN GOODS
DOWN RELIEF
UP RELIEF
UP MAIN
DOWN MAIN

4.67   4.5

5.05
5.19   5.00 Acton West

Hanger
Lane
Jn

5 : 43B
54.56

LU 1 & 3/7B : to North Acton

5.13   54.50

5 : 43B
London Underground
Piccadilly Line
to Rayners Lane

EB
WB   5.30

WP
EALING BROADWAY
(DIS) 55.51
(CEN) 54.61
[EAB] 54.61

* Local
Control Area   5.56

9 31
8 29
7 28
6 27
5
6
2 3
1

5.70
5.76

Spring
Bridge Rd
Car Park
Tunnel (121 yards)

6.08
(Longfield)

West Ealing Jn
6.54

GW (Acton & Wycombe)
WEL 1
[GW 174]
WEST EALING
6.46

4 7
3

Limit of
6.59 electrification

GW (Acton & Wycombe)
HAN
[GW 176]

Limit of
electrification
0.02

HANWELL
(& ELTHORNE)   10.00
7.28   7 3
        2

Hanwell Jn
2.19

Hanwell Jn

Wharncliffe
Viaduct
(297 yards)

River 7.43 7.38-35
Brent 7.56

Hanwell
Viaduct
(Station Rd)
(55 yards)

19A : Greenford
7.03

Plassers (AOCL) 6.71

Drayton Green Jn
[0.36]

DOWN GREENFORD

UP

Plasser &
Theurer

Engrs Sdgs

UP GOODS LOOPS   7

Hanwell Bridge Sidings
DBS

Hanwell Bridge
8
7.68
8.00
8.07
7.68

A4020
8.04

BRENTFORD GOODS 2.70

Day & Sons
European Metal Recycling

West London Waste
(Refuse Transfer Station)

2.67

2.49 P

Day & Son
GF 2.36

5 : 43B : to London Airport (Heathrow)

Southall
East Jn
8.62

Southall Jn
8.72

9

DOWN GOODS LOOP
DOWN RELIEF
UP RELIEF
UP MAIN
DOWN MAIN

8.45
8.62
8.65
8.70
8.75

SOUTHALL EAST
SIDINGS
LDD

NEW
HEAD

SHORT PIT

8.46

NEW
HEAD

LONG PIT

FUEL

9.02

Southall Railway Centre
(GWR Preservation
Group Ltd)

Cripple
Sdg   2.32

Brentford
GF 2.11

(Trumpers
Crossing)   2.07
1.39

M4

'BRENTFORD'
BRANCH'   UP

GW
BRB
[GW 178]

5 : 43B : to Acton Town

2B

B

Controlled by Slough SC (S)

Wagon
storage
only   DBS

Total Sdgs GF
(OOU)   15.76
15.57

URS

Colnbrook
Logistics
Centre (CLC)
15.56

COSTAIN SDG
HAILSTONE SDG

Total / Fina Oil
DISCHARGE SDG
LOCO RELSE
16.25

16.00

Colnbrook
16.20

LC   16.00

CD=Cement Discharge
RBD=Re-bar Discharge
PD=PFA Discharge

LANGLEY
16.18

8 4
8
4 1

M25
14.41

M25 / M4 and
interlink bridges

COLNBROOK
SINGLE

IVER
14.60

8 4
8
9 1

GW (Staines & W Drayton Rly)
STA
[GW 182]

Thorney Mill Sidings
14.10

STB
North End
14.20

CRIPPLE SDG
Bardon Aggregates
Stone terminal   14.46

STB = Stop Board

West
Drayton:
Lafarge
Aggregates

No.1 GF
OOU

No.2 GF
OOU

13.34

West Drayton
East
12.67

WEST
DRAYTON
13.17

West Drayton:
(Uxbridge Bch Jn)
13.35 (TMO)

13.39

West Drayton:
Hanson
12.21

Stockley
Bdg Jn
(12.09)

Stockley
Flyover

12.00

Slough IECC
(SN)

Slough SC (S)

Heathrow
Airport Ltd
(BAA)

NR

NR 19.295 km
BAA 19.312 km

Limit of electrification
Relief lines 18.764 km (11.51)
Main lines 19.696 km (12.09)

Heathrow
Airport Jn
11.14

HAYES &
HARLINGTON
10.71

DAWLEY UGL

UP RELIEF
DOWN RELIEF
UP MAIN
DOWN MAIN
UP AIRPORT
DOWN AIRPORT

Hayes
Up
Sidings

UB

Hayes
UGL

A312

Main Arm

Paddington
Arm

Grand
Union
Canal

Tarmac

Old HH

10.05

10.30

10.54

10.60

Platforms 1 5
          2-4 7
            5 8

HEATHROW CENTRAL
TERMINALS 1, 2 & 3
23.550 km (14.48 miles)

HEX Control Room

(Piccadilly
Line above)

1 2

T3 Escape
Shaft   24.200km

Pier 7
Escape Shaft

24.089 24.089
Crossover
Cavern)   24.032 (Up Airport)
           24.089 (Down Airport)

20.564km

Twin Tunnels

Sipson Lane 19.908km (12.30 miles)
Shepiston Lane
Escape Shaft

Custom House
Escape Shaft   22.481km

HLL
[GW 180]

London Underground District and
Piccadilly Lines to Acton Town

Controlled by Slough IECC (SN)

GW MLN 1 [GW 103]

D

From the tunnel
portals to Terminal 4
the route is marked
with indicators at
25 metre intervals

(Piccadilly Line above)

HEATHROW
TERMINAL 5
26.285 km
(16.22 miles)

3 4
10

(15.75-15.71)

IN TERMINALS

UP TERMINALS

T5C Escape Shaft
25.260km

Sealand Road
Escape Shaft   25.389km
25.8   (Change
        of Km)

HEATHROW
TERMINAL 4
26.520 km
(16.32 miles)

1 2
10

UP AIRPORT (25.8)
DN AIRPORT (26.9)

GW MLN 1 [GW 103]

Controlled by Slough IECC (SN)

C

WINDSOR & ETON CENTRAL

MAIDENHEAD
24.19
5B 5A

Engrs
24.40

HABD R. Thames
24.10 (237 yards)

Maidenhead
Viaduct
(847 yards)

Maidenhead
East   23.77

23.58

23.22-21

TAPLOW
22.39
4 9

BURNHAM
20.77
7 1 2 8

Dolphin
Junction

SLOUGH
18.36

1 2
3 4
5

17.20
17.03
17.05

17.40

Bath Rd
18.72   Windsor Bch
         (or Slough Jn)
         18.44

EAST LOOP
BAY LINE

19.12 (Chalvey)

Slough
IECC
(SN)

Slough SC (S)
18.44

Tamper Sdg

Stabling

Bruce Bishop
DBS

Coal Sdg
Engrs

UP GOODS LOOP   19.00

19.05
19.10
19.13
19.23

Slough 19
West

M4   19.43

20.05

129-285

Thames
Bridge
20.58-20.55

Windsor Viaducts
Arches 1-127   129-285
21.16   21.19

21.05

GW WIN [GW 184]

GW MLN 1 [GW 103]

WBB [GW 185]
3B : to Bourne End

Platforms 1 6
          2-5 9
              10

24.33   24.32

Platforms 9
          2-5 10

Reading SC (R) Slough SC (S)

3A : to Reading

Waltham A404(M)
WILD   25.44

(Ruscombe)
29.45
29.60

Langley
East
15.48   15.57
15.12   15.27
15.16   15.26

DOWN RELIEF
DOWN MAIN

UP RELIEF
DOWN RELIEF
UP MAIN
DOWN MAIN

16.08

UP GOODS
UP RELIEF
DOWN RELIEF
UP MAIN
DOWN MAIN

13.64
13.74

Controlled by Slough SC (S)

16.25   16

2C

2D

SOUTHALL
9.06
7 4
1

Southall
West Jn
9.70

UP RELIEF
DOWN RELIEF
UP MAIN
DOWN MAIN

SOUTHALL WEST LOOP
UP BRENTFORD SDG
DN BRENTFORD

9.57

Heathrow Airport Ltd NR
(BAA)

SHORT SPUR 0.0
(BRB)

Brentford Branch
Jn 9.06

Westinghouse
Siding

SOUTHALL WEST SIDINGS
DBS

9.70

10.05
10.19

BRB

Controlled by Slough IECC (SN)

GW MLN 1 [GW 103]

LU lines controlled from :
Earl's Court for District & Piccadilly lines
Wood Lane Service Control Centre for Central lines

LU DISTRICT LINE EB
WB
LU CENTRAL LINE

Car Sdgs (NRU)
24 25

10
9
8
6
4
2 3
1

WM   EB

© Copyright TRACKmaps. No reproduction without permission

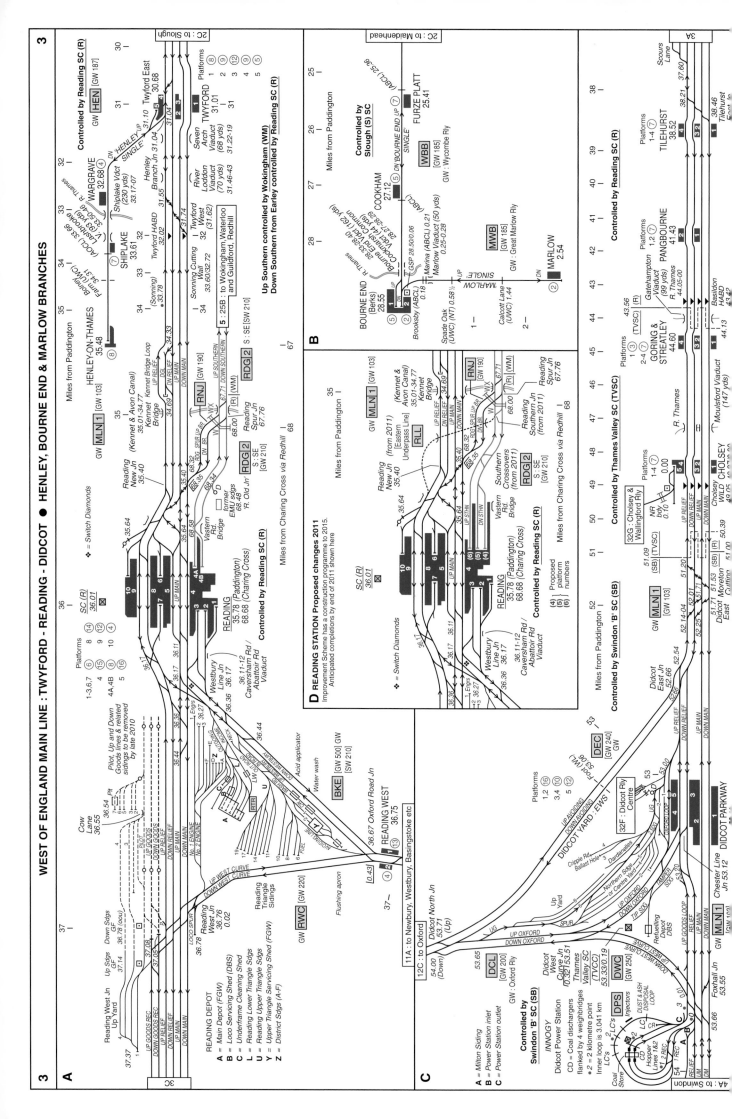

4

A

54 55 56 57 58 59 60 61 62 63 64 65 66 67 68 69 70 71 72 73 74 75 76 77 78 79 80 81 82 83 84 85 86 87 88 89 90 91 92 93 94

Didcot Terminal: Milton Freight Nedlloyd Districenters

NIRU Milton Sdg

54.70

Warehouse

Didcot Terminal: (Causeway)

Stocks Lane (CCTV) 56.58 (Causeway)

Causeway (MCB) 56.72

55.00 (Milton)

55.19 (Milton)

DGL 55.74

56.32

Steventon 55.74 (T) A34(T)

Gate box/control point

(Lockinge) 58.51

Wantage Rd HABD 59.57

Wantage Road 60.22

60.35

Butterfly Lane (UWC) 1991

60.201

Grove (UWC) 59.37

WANTAGE ROAD 60.36

Miles from Paddington

UP RELIEF RELIEF LINE UP MAIN DN MAIN

SWINDON

Highworth Jn 0.04 76.32

76.39 GW (Swindon and Highworth)

HIW [GW 470]

European Metal Recycling

North Sidings

Factory area layouts unconfirmed

BMW Group Plant: Swindon

Honda

Swindon: South Marston Eurometinal [GW 468]

Green Lane 0.20

Stratton Green 75.63

South Marston Jn 74.48

71.44 (Shrivenham)

Bourton HABD 72.20

72.36 Bourton 72.30 72.24

74.15 (Marston Crossing)

New Works Depot

Highworth GF 76.30

76.20 DRS

THRO' SDG 76.60 UP YARD LINE

UP REC

UP MAIN DOWN MAIN DOWN GOODS TWO DOWN LOOP

DBS Freight Depot

SNT

Down Yard GF 76.64

F = Freightliner

Transfer Sdgs

Controlled by Swindon SC (SN)

1 MLN 1 [GW 105] [GW 103] GW

Swindon SC Swindon 'B' SC [GW 105] (SN) (SB) GW

64½

Challow

Uffington

66.47 66.20 64.00 66.39

CHIPPENHAM 93.76

Barrow (WL) 94.01

4B

B

77

77

Controlled by Swindon 'B' SC (SB)

Platforms
1 ⑬
2 ④
3 ⑭
4 ⑮

SWINDON 77.23

UP PLATFORM DN PL

BMW

SDP

Cocklebury Sidings 77.10 DBS

UP REC UP MAIN 77.13 76.70 77.00 SPUR DOWN GDS DOWN MAIN 77.10 Down Sdgs

77.19 Swindon SC (SN)

Swindon Jn 77.36

UP KEMBLE 77.48 DOWN KEMBLE

UP & DN GDS 77.45

77.49

GW [GW 480] SWM 1

15A : to Stroud

Ø change of line designation

77.60 Swindon 'B' SC (SB)

NB: Does not control the area Bristol side of 64½ MP

(former MSW over) 78.50

Rushey Platt 78.36

GW MLN 1 [GW 105]

M4 W 80.00 E (Hay Lane)

Studley HABD 81.40

Wootton Bassett Jn 82.72

83.07

SOUTH WALES AND BRISTOL DIRECT LINE

14C : to Bristol Parkway

GW SWB [GW 600]

UGL 83.29 83.28

UP DOWN BADMINTON

Wootton Bassett GF

Stone shute Foster Yeoman

❖ = Switch Diamonds

GW MLN 1 [GW 105]

(Christian Malford) 89.74

91.00 90.77

River Avon Viaduct (72 yards)

(Dauntsey)

87.57

Controlled by Swindon SC (SN)

Miles from Paddington

77 78 79 80 81 82 83 84 85 86 87 88 89 90 91 92 93 94

⑫

1 2

4C

5A : to Bristol

C

Miles from Paddington

94.13-08 95 96 97 98 99 100 101 102 103 104 105 106 107 108 109 110 111 112 113

Chippenham Viaduct (90 yards)

Thingley Jn 96.10 Swindon SC (W) Westbury SC (W)

94.13-08

95.25

LCU (Local Control Unit)

96.10 95.35

Rail Recycling Centre

96.34

Bristol SC (B)

GW MLN [GW 105]

(Corsham) 98.26

^ Box 99.12 Summit

Box Tunnel (1 mile, 1452 yards) 101.48-39

Middle Hill Tunnel (198 yards) 100.78

(Box) 101.69

(Bathford) 103.76

Bathampton Jn 104.45 (Up)

104.41 104.55

Dolemeads Viaduct (355 yds) 106.60-49

Sydney Gardens West Tunnel (99 yards) 106.33-29

Sydney Gardens East Tunnel (77 yards) 106.28-24

Arches & St James Viaduct (600 yards) 107.20-106.68

BATH SPA 106.71

Bath Westmoreland Rd Bath & N.E. Somerset Council Refuse Transfer Stn Bath Goods 107.47

Bath West GF 107.69

OLDFIELD PARK 107.72

107.28 107.33

Twerton Viaduct (638 yards) 108.58-29

Twerton 108.09 (S&D) 108.60 over

Twerton Long Tunnel (264 yards) 109.13-03

Twerton Short Tunnel (45 yards) 108.72-70

(Saltford) 111.27

Saltford Tunnel (176 yards) 111.65-57

(Avon Valley Rly) see 32C

Manor Farm (UWC) 99.33

(Laycock) 97.12

97.13

100 UP MELKSHAM

MELKSHAM 100.13

GW (Wilts, Somerset & Weymouth)

WEY [GW 523]

SINGLE

DN MELKSHAM

NB: Change of Line direction from Melksham Single

♦ Change of Line direction from Melksham Single

Frying Pan Fm 101.10

Church Fm No.1 (UWC) 101.80

Church Fm No.2 (UWC) 102.10

Avon View Fm (UWC) 103.09

Steventon (UWC) 103.60

102.54 Avon Fm (Holt Jn)

Bradford Jn 9.12/104.40 (S)

11C

★ *

UP (N)

DN (W)

Bradford Vt (159 yds) 7.18-25

Greenland Mill (77 yds) 7.27

Tucker's 7.01 (R. Avon)

Greenland Mill (UWC) 8.18

Cemetery Lane (UWC) 8.01

Westbrd SC (W)

Freshford SC (W)

Bradford Jn's

11

11B

6.77

8 ⑥

7

Avoncliffe Add (14 yds) 5.71

Avoncliffe Vdct (K & A) 5.70

6.27 7.01 5.08

AVONCLIFF 5.63

FRESHFORD 4.70

Fisher's (BW5)(UWC) 4.01

Young's (BW4)(UWC) 3.25

Glass' (BW2)(UWC) 0.20

(Limpley Stoke)

Claverton (BW3)(UWC) 1.73

Dundas Aquaduct (K & A Canal) 3.12

0.00

4 3 2 1 —1 —2

UP TROWBRIDGE DN TROWBRIDGE

UPL DM UM

BFB [GW 510]

GW (Wilts, Somerset & Weymouth)

Bristol SC (B)

4B

Controlled by Bristol SC (B)

* Former Bradford Jn's

(N) formerly Bradford North Jn 104.11
(S) formerly Bradford South Jn
(W) former Bradford West Jn 8.64

4

August 2010

© Copyright TRACKmaps. No reproduction without permission

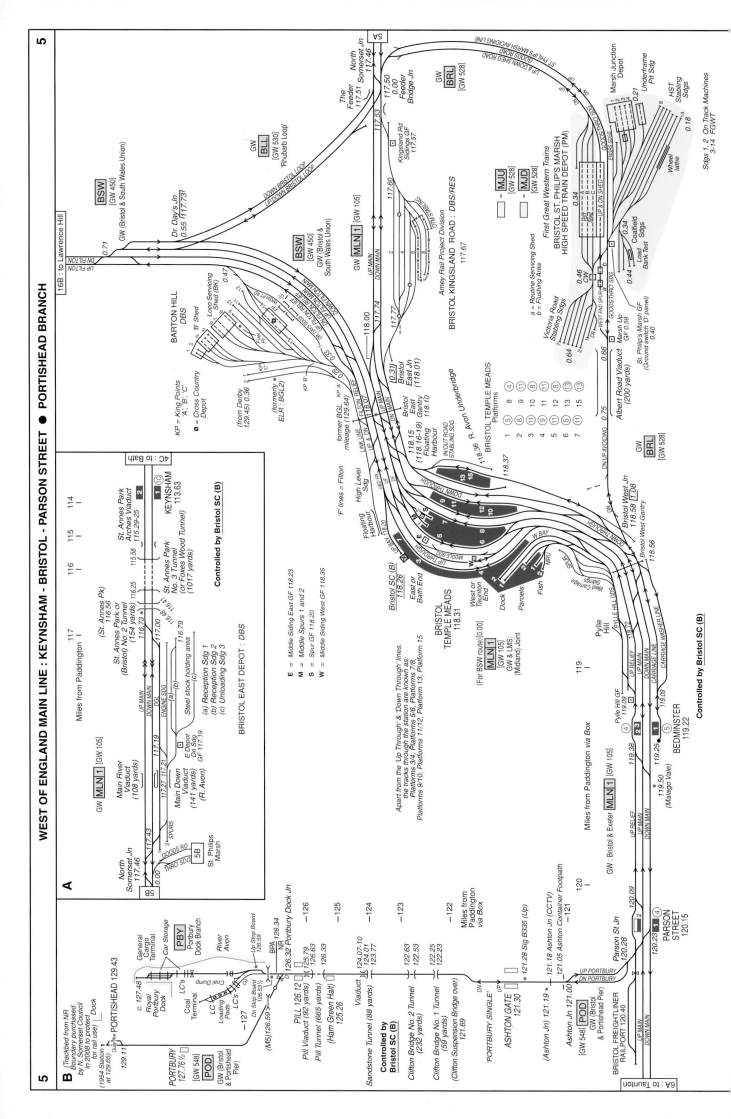

WEST OF ENGLAND MAIN LINE : KEYNSHAM - BRISTOL - PARSON STREET ● PORTISHEAD BRANCH

WEST OF ENGLAND MAIN LINE : (PARSON STREET) - TAUNTON - TIVERTON PARKWAY ● WEST SOMERSET RAILWAY

A

5B : to Bristol

122.08 (Long Ashton)
123.66-61 123.00
Flax Bourton Tunnel (110 yards)

UP MAIN
DOWN MAIN

Miles from Paddington via Box

Lines to Cogload (excl.) controlled by Bristol (B) SC

(Brent Knoll) 142.43

GW : Bristol & Exeter MLN 1 [GW 105]
UP MAIN
DOWN MAIN

WESTON-SUPER-MARE 137.33
137.22 Up GF Carriage Sdgs
GW : Bristol & Exeter WSM [GW 107]
137.14
137.58
WESTON-SUPER-MARE AVOIDING
UP WESTON
DOWN WESTON

138.04 Uphill Jn
139.05

Huish (BC13) (PX) Yatton 132.11
Stone House Lane (BC8)(UWC) 131.49
Mud Lane (BC9)(UWC) 130.49
Yatton GF 131.05
Yatton West 131.20
YATTON 130.28
Yatton East
NAILSEA & BACKWELL 126.33
Nailsea HABD 127.41

Puxton & Worle 133.79 (MGB)
133.47 M5
133.42 (PX) (Control Point)
WESTON MILTON 136.12
WORLE 134.42
135.11 Worle Jn
135.65

B

Miles from Paddington via Box

HIGHBRIDGE & BURNHAM-ON-SEA 145.25
145.19
145.60 Highbridge East
145.65 Highbridge West

Pawlett Meads (BC4)(UWC) 147.07
Humspill (BC33)(UWC) 147.44

(Dunball) 149.05

Weighbridge GF 151.33
BRIDGWATER YARD
Freight Sidings
Gantry
Devonshire Street
Bridgwater Station GF 151.44
BRIDGWATER 151.47
151.38

Lines to Cogload (excl.) controlled by Bristol SC (B)

GW : Bristol & Exeter MLN 1 [GW 108] [GW 105]
UP MAIN
DOWN MAIN
Exeter SC (E) | Bristol SC (B)
UP BRISTOL
DOWN BRISTOL

Meads (BC39)(RG-X) 152.68
152.60 M5
152.03

Fordgate 154.12

(Durston) 157.29
157.58
UP ATHELNEY
DOWN ATHELNEY
137.60
Cogload Jn-Up 158.23 138.03
Cogload Jn-Down 158.50 138.30
Cogload HABD 158.70

12B : to Castle Cary
CCL [GW 500]

Controlled by Exeter SC (E)

GW : Bristol & Exeter MLN 1 [GW 108]
UP MAIN
DOWN MAIN
Taunton East Jn 162.35
161.03 M5
Broomhay (BH52)(UWC) 161.32
Hyde Farm (BH53)(UWC) 160.75

C WEST SOMERSET RAILWAY PLC

MINEHEAD 187.71
Loco Shed & Workshop
Carriage Wkshop
STONE SDG
MAIN
BAY
Bay Sidings
187.76 187.55
187.72

D WEST SOMERSET RAILWAY PLC

GW : B & E West Somerset Rly former MIN

BISHOPS LYDEARD 168.20
LOCO SDGS
Pits Bay Sdg
UP SDGS
Visitor Centre & Museum
168.17 168.09 DN South GF
UP LOOP
DOWN
MINEHEAD
SINGLE
168.06

Roebuck Gate (AOCL) 172.88
CROWCOMBE HEATHFIELD 172.10
UP LOOP
MN
Summit

Leigh Wood (AOCL) 173.48

Whiteball Tunnel (1092 yards)
Whiteball Summit
174.58 173.63
173.13
Badcock's Middle (BH34)(UWC) 175.44

STOGUMBER 174.64
(Burlescombe)

Westford (Cutlers) Property (RG) 170.58
Nynehead HABD 168.59
Bradford-on-Tone (AHBC) 167.33
(Wellington) 170.19

WILLITON 178.06
WSRA Workshop
178.18 Williton GF
178.15
Diesel & Electric Preservation Group

TIVERTON PARKWAY 177.28
177.15 (A361, North Devon Link Road)
Visitor Centre
177.18 173.63
Sampford Peverell Halt (⌀ on site of former)
178.52

D (Taunton area)

former GW MINEHEAD BRANCH

(Request) DONIFORD HALT 178.75
Goviers Lane Footpath (RG)(G) 179.58
WATCHET 179.64
WASHFORD 182.11
Somerset & Dorset Railway Trust Museum
182.13

BLUE ANCHOR 184.34
184.2

Sea Lane 186.09
Camping Coach Sdg

DUNSTER 186.21
Civil Engrs Depot
186.23 GF
Dunster West 186.38 (udo)
Dunster West GF 186.38
Seaward (AOCL) 187.50

UP RELIEF
DOWN MAIN
DOWN RELIEF
TAUNTON 163.12
Taunton West Jn 163.34
Loco Sdgs
BAY SDG
Barrow (WL) 163.02

GW : Bristol & Exeter MLN 1 [GW 108]
UP MAIN
DOWN MAIN

Miles from Paddington via Box

FAIRWATER YARD
High Output Ballast Cleaning Yd 164.00
FAIRWATER HEADSHUNT
163.61
164.24
GOODS RECEPTION
DOWN UP RELIEF
164.35 A3605 (Silk Mill)
164.60
Norton Fitzwarren Jn
[GW 602]
Token board 164.69
165.20 WSR NR
165.08 (Norton Fitzwarren)
NORTON FITZWARREN 165.43
Turning Triangle
Allerford Jn 165.60
Darby's Crossing 167.63
Victory (AHBC) 166.04

7A : to Exeter

Miles from Paddington via Box

MIN

West Somerset Railway Trust Museum

Network Rail lines to Cogload (incl.) controlled by Exeter SC (E)

August 2010.

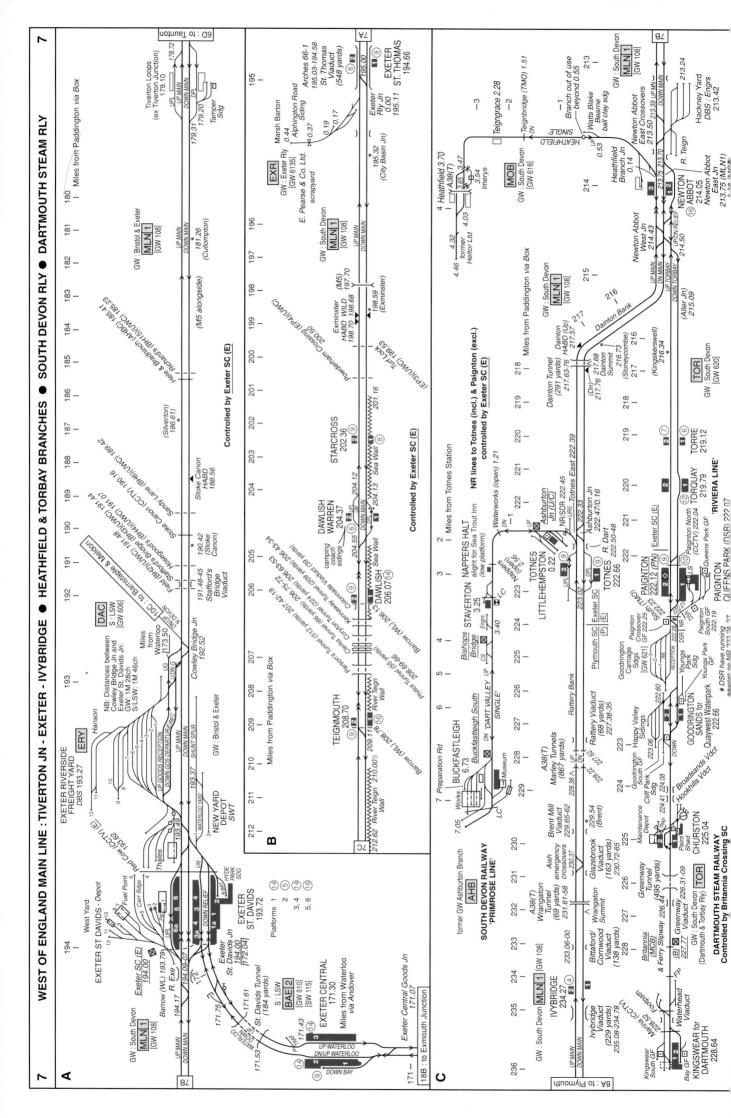

8

WEST OF ENGLAND MAIN LINE : (IVYBRIDGE) - PLYMOUTH - SALTASH ● CATTEWATER BRANCH ● GUNNISLAKE BRANCH ● PLYM VALLEY RAILWAY

8

D

Miles from Paddington via Box

236 237 238 239 240 241 242 243 244 245

7C : to Newton Abbot

(Cornwood) 237.48 Blatchford Viaduct (309 yards)
237.27-13
Slade Viaduct (257 yards)
237.69-57

GW : South Devon   MLN 1 [GW 108]

239.07
239.13 Hemerdon (P) GSP
239.29 UGL
239.40
Hemerdon Bank

241.75 (Plympton)

SHUNT 242.42
SPUR

242.55

242.60

TAVISTOCK JUNCTION YARD : DBS   TJY

On track machine maintenance shed

Tavistock Jn GF 242.69

End of Line 243.50
Marsh Mills China Clay Wks
Imerys (mothballed)

Marsh Mills No. 2 (TOC)
Marsh Mills No. 1 (TOC) 243.06

Continued on left inset

MARSH MILLS 0.24
MARSH MILLS 0.27

LAN 1
GW 626
GW : S. Devon & Tavistock
Vehicle ramp

243.25 243.16
243.67
243.10 243.14
R. Plym

PLYMBRIDGE HALT c. 1.39

proposed extension

PLYM VALLEY RAILWAY

end of Line 1.06
Lee Moor China Clay Crossing 1.07
Operating Limit 1.05
0.56 (World's End)
LAN 2
GW : South Devon and Tavistock

0.24 OOU
MARSH MILLS 0.27

Marsh Mills North Jn 0.44

A

Lipson Jn 244.35
0.00
UP MAIN
DOWN MAIN

Speedway Goods Branch (AOCL) 244.27
244.60

Speedway Jn 0.18/244.30

Laira Jn 243.78
A374(T)

GW : South Devon   MLN 1 [GW 108]

DOWN MAIN
UP MAIN
DOWN GOODS
OCEAN SDG 243.54
243.28 243.67
Sea Wall
Laira Jn 244.02

Controlled by Plymouth SC (P)

Through Sidings
Embankment Carriage Sidings   LAS [GW 629]

Lipson Sidings
DOWN / UP GOODS

PLYMOUTH (LAIRA) TRACTION MAINTENANCE DEPOT (LA)

First Great Western

Workshops
HST Shed
LC

E = 'Eurostar UK'
M = Maintenance Bldg.
U = Underframe Cleaning
PLO [GW 628]
SUT

244.41 (mileage change, - 4 chains)
Mount Gould Jn

TUR S : LSW
CWR S : LSW

S : LSW
Laira Viaduct (222 yards)

Cattewater Jn 0.43
Operational Limit 0.68

Speedway Jn (to Speedway Jn)
UP/DOWN
DOWN / UP
PLYMOUTH LOOP No. 1

(Friary Jn) 244.60
(244.45)
0.34
FRY SUT [GW 628]

European Metals Recycling
Turnchapel Branch Jn
End of Line 0.73

FRY [GW 628]
S : LSW
PLYMOUTH FRIARY DBS 245.39
245.17/0.00
245.22 245.25
245.17

RIVER PLYM

Shapters Way (TMO) 1.16
Cattedown Tunnel (48 yards)
1.24 1.26 1.30 1.39
1.43 1.44
former Conoco Terminal

B

Miles from Paddington via Box

245

(Lipson Vale) UP M 245.08
DN M

8A

Plymouth East GF   245.46 245.32
ENGRS SDG 245.56
SS DN SDG 245.48 245.56
SS Mutley Tunnel (317 yards), inc. 134 yards of elevated car park)

Platforms 3 (4)
4, 5 (15)
6 (13)
7, 8 (15)

Park or Up Sdgs

7 8   5 6   THROUGH LINE   4   4 3 2 1

PLYMOUTH (former North Road) 245.75

Car Park LC

former Cornwall Loop Jn (from Millbay)
2 MLN 1 [GW 108]
(CORNWALL LOOP)

COM 247.42 246.29
246.25-19 Cornwall Loop Vdct (131 yards)
247.54 (former Devonport Jn) [230.12]
248.42-37
SC (P) 246.04

UP MAIN
DOWN MAIN
247.42

Drake House LC

DDB

'ADMIRALTY PLATFORM' (Wixons Jn)

NORTH YARD (EXTENSION) YARD
Qy

Limit of Dockyard shunt
248.76-68

Keyham East GF 247.97
Keyham HABD 247.87 (161 yards)
DEVONPORT Tnl (117 yards)
Keyham Vdct 248.77 248.60
248.28

* = Dockyard Junction 249.41 miles from Paddington via Box and Plymouth (Millbay)
♦ = Miles from Waterloo via Okehampton

(Miles from Waterloo via Okehampton)
-- 226

KEYHAM 249.25
6
Keyham West GF 249.38
248.79 (Ford)
248.76-68

227.02
ST. BUDEAUX VICTORIA ROAD

Tamar Bridge 226.22 A38(T)
226.26

ST. BUDEAUX FERRY ROAD 250.15
Single Line Jn

St. Budeaux Jn 250.77 [227.57]
249.63-46
Dockyard Jn (or Keyham) 249-41
Weston Mill Vdct (375 yards)
249.70

250.70 250.32
250.25
250 250.26

8C

SALTASH 251.26
MLN 2 [GW 108]
GW : Cornwall

252 Miles from Paddington via Box and Plymouth (Millbay)

Controlled by Plymouth SC (P)

9A : to Liskeard

Coombe by Saltash Viaduct (205 yards) 251.47-38
251.23 251.11 251.04 250.77 250.09
251.26
Royal Albert Bridge (730 yards)

DOWN MAIN
UP MAIN

ROYAL ALBERT BRIDGE (Opened 1859)
Cornwall App. Main Spans Devon App. Spans
2 Main spans each 455ft long
Rails 103ft above high water level

C

Miles from Waterloo via Okehampton

226 225 224 223 222 221 220

Ernesettle Sidings Ministry of Defence (Navy)
South GF 225.79
North GF 225.58
DN 'GUNNISLAKE' 'SINGLE' UP
8B

DAC [GW 637] S : LSW (Devon & Cornwall)

224.38 224.15
River Tavy Viaduct (497 yards)
Tamerton Viaduct (117 yards) 224.01 225.01

222.69 BERE FERRERS
5

Collins Farm (UWC) 220.31
Bere Alston Jn 0.02/220.07
Bere Alston GF 220.07
0.00/220.05
BERE ALSTON
Helston Farm (UWC) 1.52-1.38
1.55
[GW 637] DAC

CALSTOCK 1.55
Calstock Viaduct (290 yards)
Okeltor (open) 2.28
Sandways (open) 3.31
CAL [GW 637]
GUNNISLAKE 4.40
5

S : Plymouth, Devonport & SW Jn
'Bere Alston & Callington Light'
'THE TAMAR VALLEY LINE'

No. 1; (UWC) 1.38
4 3 2 1

Controlled by Plymouth SC (P)

DEVONPORT ROYAL DOCKYARD
Devonport Royal Dockyard Ltd.
Original detail for North Yard
courtesy of Paul Burkhalter (2005)

RIVER TAMAR
HAMOAZE

No. 4 Basin
No. 5 Basin
No. 8 Dock No. 9 Dock No. 10 Dock
No. 14 Dock No. 15 Dock

Weston Mill Lake

Fleet Maintenance Base
Submarine Refit Complex

Rails in situ but not connected

Limit of BR shunt
Barrier
Gantry
(former BR operating limit) Exchange Sidings

Detached sidings which remain mostly been omitted.

August 2010

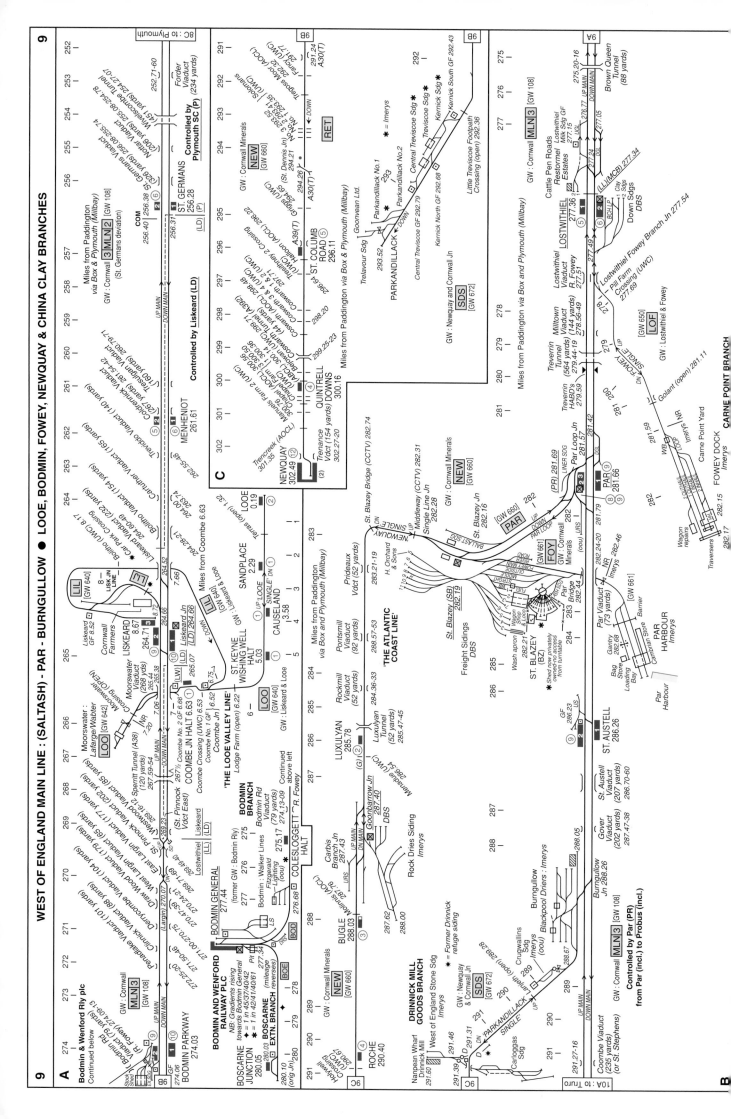

WEST OF ENGLAND MAIN LINE : (BURNGULLOW) - PENZANCE ● FALMOUTH & ST. IVES BRANCHES ● NORTH DEVON LINE

GW : Cornwall MLN 3 [GW 108]
Miles from Paddington via Box and Plymouth (Millbay)

9B : to St. Austell

Fal Viaduct (177 yards) 291.67-59 (Millbay)

293.17 (Grampound Rd)

295.29 (Probus) Par (PR)

Truro (T)

Tregagle Viaduct (581 yards)
Tregarne Viaduct (182 yards)
Polperro Tunnel (94 yards) 296.59-52
297.11-07

Buckshead Tunnel (320 yards) 297.76-50
UP MAIN / DOWN MAIN
299.25-10

Carnedas Viaduct (264 yards) 300.29-09
Truro Viaduct (439 yards)
300.51-39 (T) 300.57 TRURO 300.63

Higher-town tunnel (70 yards) 301.13-10
Sparnick Tunnel (491 yards)

'THE MARITIME LINE'

Penwithers Jn 301.25
Paradise (UWC) 302.16
302.13-10

Penwithers Viaduct (139 yards) 302

'FALMOUTH BRANCH SINGLE' 303.10 304
PERRANWELL 304.78
Carnon (New) Viaduct (253 yards) 304.26-38
Perran Viaduct (New) (79 yards) 305.74-70

Ponsanooth (New) Viaduct (220 yards) 306
Perran Tunnel (374 yards) 307.52 307.53 COM 3 FAL 2 [GW 680]
306.40-23 (Penryn Deviation)

PENRYN 309.10
Collegewood Viaduct (300 yards) 309.45-32 309.23 309.24 COM 4 MLN 3

PENMERE 311.13 4

FALMOUTH TOWN 312.09
Falmouth No. 1 GF 312.22
Falmouth No. 2 GF 312.37
FALMOUTH DOCKS 312.46
A & P Appledore (Falmouth) Ltd.
NIRU 312.51

ST. IVES BRANCHES

St. Ives Viaduct (106 yards) 325.02-07 — 325
Carbis Viaduct (78 yards) 324.03-07 — 324
CARBIS BAY 323.78
Hawkes Point (FP) (NT) 323.46 — 323
'ST. IVES SINGLE' Towan (UWC) 322.63 — 322
ST. IVES 325.13 [GW 690] SIV
GW : St. Ives Branch Rly

'THE ST IVES BAY LINE'

Western Growers Crossing (NT) 321.08
LELANT 322.06
LELANT SALTINGS 321.49
ST. ERTH 320.78
Hayle Vdct (277 yards) 319.35-31
Hayle Jn 321.02
Guildford Viaduct (123 yards) 319.34
Angarrack Viaduct (235 yards) 316.32
Lower Tenowin (UWC) 316.35
U. Tenowin (UWC) 316.52
HAYLE 319.31
GW : W. Cornwall MLN 4 [GW 108]

Miles from Paddington via Box and Plymouth (Millbay)
LONG ROCK DEPOT (East End) (FGW)
Penzance HST Depot (PZ) (FGW)
325.00 Single Line Jn
Long Rock (CCTV) 325.12
Marazion 324.55
PONSANDANE (West End) DBS
Loading Banks 325.60
Sandy Kings
PENZANCE 326.50
Oil Sidings
Motorail Ramp

NORTH DEVON LINE

NEWTON ST. CYRES 176.51 [GW 606] DAC
Norton 1 (UWC) (E) 173.50
Cowley Bridge Jn (a) 173.64 (b) 192.52
7A : to Taunton
7A : to Exeter

Flood Arches (50 yards) 177.22-20
Newton St. Cyres HABD 176.60
Crediton (CN) [MCB] 178.25
Freight Sdgs
CREDITON 179.20 Crediton SB SC
179.32

Miles from Waterloo via Andover

Salmon Pool (AOCL) 180.00
Stockeydown Farm (UWC) 181.70
YEOFORD 182.72
(Coleford Jn) 183.69 [GW 609] [GW 608] DAC
COPPLESTONE 185.67
Common Moor 1 (UWC) 187.04
BOW 187.55
Common Moor 2 (UWC) 188.34
MORCHARD ROAD 187.38
NORTH TAWTON 190.65
North Tawton Viaduct (62 yards) 194.24-21
SAMPFORD COURTENAY 193.50
Fatherford Viaduct 196.47-43
LAPFORD 189.65 [GW 606] NDN S : LSW
Lapford North 189.57 Lapford South 189.73

'THE TARKA LINE'

Alfordon (UWC) 195.14 Alfordon (UWC) 195.12
OKEHAMPTON 197.25 Okehampton GF 197.33 197.51
A30 (T)
Newcombes (UWC) 198.99
Chenson No. 1 (UWC) 191.24
Chenson No. 2 (UWC) 191.62
Chenson No. 3 (UWC) 192.08
EGGESFORD 193.57 193.71
Portsmouth Arms (TMO) 193.54 193.49
DARTMOOR RAILWAY
(Summer Sundays)

BARNSTAPLE section
BARNSTAPLE 211.25 211.31 SDT 211.18
210.78 A39 (T) R. Taw
210.50 A39 (T) 210.29 R. Taw
Beare Vdct 208.41-40
Great Fisherton Farm No. 2 (UWC) 207.72
Great Fisherton Farm No. 1 (UWC) 207.62-66
Black Viaduct (75 yards) 207.23 No. 1
CHAPELTON 207.02
207.06 (UWC)
Fishley (UWC) 206.43
Umberleigh Barton No. 3 (UWC) 205.70
Controlled by Crediton SB (CN)
Umberleigh River Viaduct (70 yds) 204.65-68
UMBERLEIGH 204.52
Umberleigh (AOCL) 204.32
Brightley Barton No. 1 (UWC) 204.00
Brightley Mill (UWC) 203.66
Brightley Weir Farm (UWC) 203.44 No. 3
203.34 No. 2 203.23 No. 1
Shortridge Farm (62 yards) (R. Taw) 202.71 No. 3
202.54 No. 2
Weirmarsh Viaduct (62 yards) (R. Taw) 202.34-37
Harris Farm (UWC) 202.11
Scoop Viaduct (73 yards) (R. Taw) 201.47 No. 1
Scoop Viaduct (68 yards) (R. Taw) 201.35-39
Kingford Viaduct 200.61-64
PORTSMOUTH ARMS 200.38 No. 2 Portsmouth Arms (UWC)
Collaton Barton Farm No. 1 (UWC)
Higher Doomsford (UWC) 198.59
Braggamarsh No. 2 (UWC) 199.42
Braggamarsh No. 1 (UWC) 199.15
KINGS NYMPTON 197.51
Newnham1 196.02
Barton Farm 198.01

CAMBORNE / REDRUTH section
Camborne CCTV 313.20 Bostwell Jn (B) 313.35
Dolcoath (AHBC) 312.82
Penponds Viaduct (120 yards) 314.54-49
CAMBORNE 313.40
Blackwater Viaduct (127 yards) 305.33
Chacewater Viaduct (94 yards) (UWC) 305.33
305.73-68
Chacewater Deviation 305.65 COM
GW : West Cornwall [GW 108]
Baldhu SB 304.02
REDRUTH 309.68
Redruth Tunnel (190 yards) 309.64-62
Redruth Viaduct (190 yards) 310.08-309.79
Drump Lane 309.25
Penwithers 302.68

DARTMOOR RAILWAY
MELDON QUARRY 199.06 Barton Aggregates 199.06
Meldon Vdct 198.99
Meldon 199.35 199.39
Newcombes (UWC) 198.99

© Copyright TRACKmaps. No reproduction without permission

August 2010

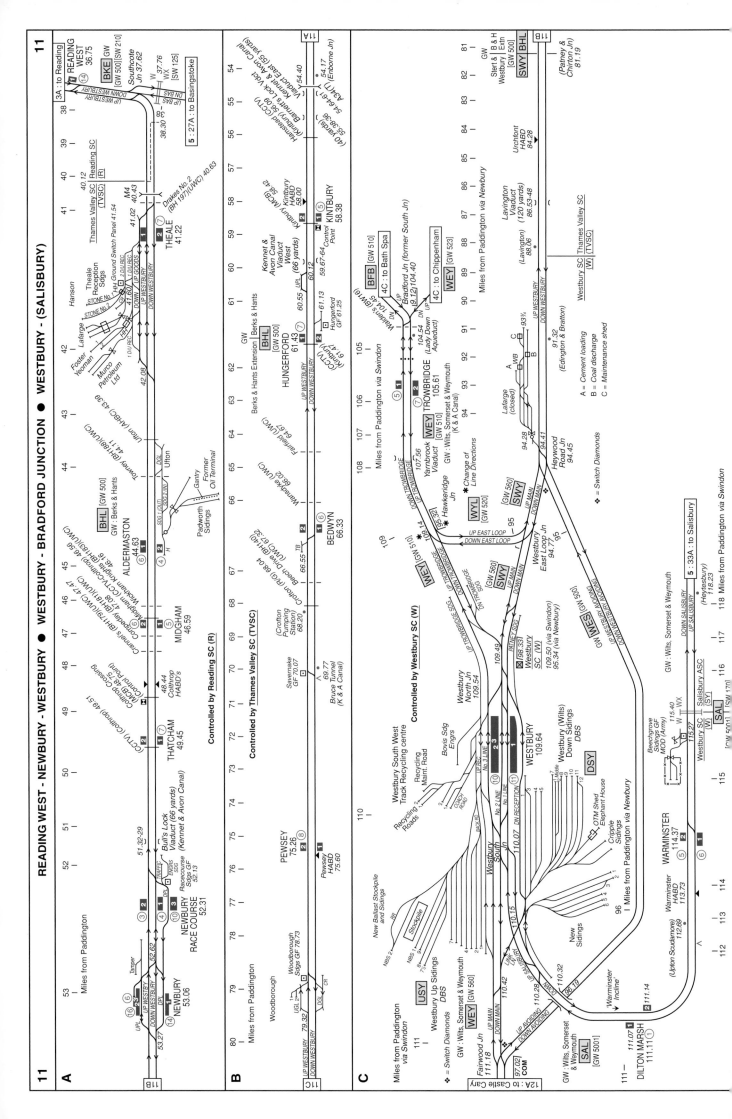

A

EAST SOMERSET RAILWAY (D. Shepherd)

D SOMERSET & DORSET RAILWAY HERITAGE TRUST
MIDSOMER NORTON
SOUTH
S (LSW) & LMS (Mid) Jt
4' 8½" gauge
Temporary [SAD]
Miles from Bath Jn
12.00 11.78 Foot
Stock Loading/unloading Sdg
Loco Shed (former Goods Shed)
Loading Dock
future connection and sidings
12.29 To Chilcompton

CRANMORE
Carriage shed
ESR | NR
5.48
LCE ES LC
Signal Box GF 6.00
Station GF 5.60
Gates GF 6.00 (operates double track trailing points at NR/ESR boundary)
Art Gallery & Museum
5.69 GF 5.60
CRANMORE 5.57 (owned by ESR)
CRANMORE WEST 5.72
EAST SOMERSET RAILWAY (D. Shepherd)
continued top left
MENDIP VALE 7.40
7½
MERRYFIELD LANE 6.53

Miles from Paddington via Swindon

BRUTON 126.09
125.69 Bruton HABD
127.39 (former S & D overbridge)
Platforms 1, 2
3
CASTLE CARY 129.45
129.14
Castle Cary Jn 129.17
115.32 (via Newbury)
129.50 (via Swindon)
COM
17B 12B

GW : Wilts, Somerset & Weymouth
[WEY] [GW 500]

WHITES CROSSING SDG
Cranmore East GF 5.48
Whites Crossing
NR limit 4.58 (Sdg only)
Merehead West 4.57
5.18
[ESB] [GW 580] GW : East Somerset
CHEDDAR VALLEY LINE

MEREHEAD STONE TERMINAL
Foster Yeoman Quarries Ltd
Torr Works
Travelling loader
'Mendip Rail Ltd'
Departure tracks (4-6)
Arrival tracks (1-3)
Chord Line
MEREHEAD EAST CURVE
MEREHEAD QUARRY BRANCH
former Wagon Works
Wheel drop pit
Wheel Gallery
WB
Probotec Maintenance Depot
3 - Inspection Pit
4 - Fuel Point

RADSTOCK
8.08
'Norton Radstock Regeneration Co.'
(NORTH SOMERSET RAILWAY)

WHATLEY QUARRY BRANCH
Whatley Quarry
Hanson Quarry Products, Europe Ltd
'Mendip Rail Ltd'
Loco Shed
Wagon Repairs
LC
Mells Road
[FNS] 2
[WQL]
5.02 - 4.70
Belt

Bedlam Tunnel (275 yards) 2.64-51
Great Elm Tunnel (319 yards)
Murdercombe Tunnel (55 yards)
[WQLFNS] 2
Hapsford GF OOU 2.38
NR 2.40
From 4MP absorbed by part of National Cycle Network, Route 24.
3.11-2.76
3.58-56

FROME 115.44
[FNS] 1
Frome West 0.00 FROME
Frome North Jn 115.19
115.24
Blatchbridge Jn 116.37
COM
116.52 [WEY]
DOWN WESTBURY
UP WESTBURY

[FNS] 2 (Leonard's Mill Viaduct (62 yards) 1.25
'WHATLEY QUARRY SINGLE'
Gas House Viaduct (41 yards) 0.66
North Row Viaduct (46 yards) 0.51
Willow Vale Viaduct (37 yards) 0.30
Mineral Loop
Frome West
GW : Wilts, Somerset & Weymouth [GW 572]
[WEY] [GW 500]

Master's (BH54) 111.53
Fairwood Jn 97.02
11C : to Westbury
111.18

Clink Road Jn 114.44
Frome North Jn 115.19 (former Mineral Loop Jn)
DOWN FROME AVOIDING
GW [FRA] [GW 500]

B

[ESB] [GW 580]
Brewham Summit 122.52
GW : East Somerset
Forestry (UWC) 4.15
Probotec
Cross Cottage (UWC) 2.51
(Wanstrow) 2.26
121.38

East Somerset Jn 120.73
'Witham' 120.64
UP/DOWN BRANCH LOOP 120.50
120.45
0.11
120.73
'MEREHEAD SINGLE'
Merehead Jn 3.50
NR limit 3.67
Up Sdgs
Merehead Halt

MEREHEAD West 4.57

Denning's (BH79) 122.01
Brewham Summit

Cogload Jn Up 158.23
138.30 158.50 (via Newbury) 138.50 (via Bristol)
Cogload Jn Down 138.03

6B : to Taunton
6B : to Bridgwater

TOLSCO (MMC 9)
BRISTOL 158.04
137.60

Miles from Paddington via Newbury, Westbury and Frome (not via Avoiding Lines)
Controlled by Westbury SC (W)

Exeter (E) | Westbury (W)
SC | SC
Engrs

Somerton Viaduct (116 yards)
(R. Cary) 125.20-15
125.56 (Somerton)
Somerton GF 126.11
Somerton Tunnel (1053 yards)
126.59 127.27 126.50
UP ATHELNEY
DOWN ATHELNEY

Langport (or Foal Mead) Viaduct (211 yards) 130.24-14
(Curry Rivel Jn) (Langport East) 129.73
130.72 (Curry Rivel Jn)

Hollies Moor (UWC) 133.31
Curits Dove (UWC) 135.00
Athelney (AHBD) 134.79
(BH57/UWC)

Controlled by Exeter SC (E)

CASTLE CARY 129.45
12A
Castle Cary Jn 129.50
115.32
COM
3 2
17B : to Yeovil Pen Mill

Passanage Farm (UWC) 117.10
(BH69)
Keinton Mandeville HABD 120.06
120.21
East Lydford Jn 122.31
(Charlton Mackrell)
[CCL] [GW 500]
UP ATHELNEY
DOWN ATHELNEY
GW

C

Miles from Paddington via Didcot

OXFORD 63.41
Dock Sdgs
SC [OX] 63.46
63.60
Oxford Old Loco Sidings
Up Carriage Sidings
Down Carriage Sidings
Station (Botley Rd) 63.31
West Midlands Sidings/ Cemetery Sidings
New Ballast Stockpile
[OXD] [GW 276]
LMS : LNW
Oxford North Jn 30.00 30.09
DN JERICHO
UP LINE
DOWN MAIN
UP MAIN
64.33 64.45
64.00
30
7
* = Internal user only

13B : to Banbury 13A : to Bicester Town

HINKSEY YARD 62.22
Local Distribution Centre
Hinksey South 61.74
Hinksey North 62.50
61.53
Kennington Jn 61.08
61.04
Manor Farm (UWC) 60.49
Radley HABD 60.00
RADLEY 58.35
Millstream Jn 61.79
(R. Thames) Kennington Jn
Tuckwells
R. Isis 62.79
U&DPL
(R. Thames)
Hinksey Rec Line GF 62.09
GW : Oxford Rly [DCL] [GW 200]
No. 1 RECEPTION
No. 2 RECEPTION
No. 3 THRO
No. 4 THRO
No. 5 THRO
No. 6 MS
2 SOUTH
4 SOUTH
6 SOUTH
CRIPPLE
New Ballast Stockpile
UP MAIN
DOWN MAIN
DN SOUTH

GW : Oxford Rly [DCL] [GW 200]

Controlled to Appleford (excl.) by Oxford SC (OX)

Miles from Princes Risborough
16 17 18
18.25 18.29 18.36 18.45
Miles from Paddington via Princes Risborough

Morris Cowley GF 16.04
'COWLEY SINGLE'
CRIPPLE
RR LOOP
GW : Wycombe Extension
Oxford SC (OX) [OX] (SB)
Swindon 'B' SC 57.29-24
Nuneham Viaduct (99 yards)
[SB]
[THA] [GW 260]
Keinton...
DOWN OXFORD
UP OXFORD 8

CULHAM 56.17
4 (OX)
55.43-39 55.16 4
Appleford (UWC) 60.49

D

COWLEY
BMW Car Terminal / STVA
Loading Roads
15.80 15.15 15.25
[12A]
3 2

17B : to Yeovil Pen Mill (W)
Controlled by Westbury SC (W)

APPLEFORD
Appleford (CCTV)
Appleford GF 54.33
54.00 53.71
Didcot North Jn
55.32 54 55 56 57 58 59 60 61 62 63 64 65
APPLEFORD (GW 254)
Hanson
Appleford (95 yards) (R. Thames)
1 & 2 Rubbish (Freightliner, Crane)
3 & 4 Stone
* Stone Heap and Ballast Stockpile between 3 and 4
CRIPPLE
(SB) (OX)
5 (5)
[DCL] [GW 200]
[12]

3C : to Didcot
13B : to Banbury 13A : to Bicester Town

(DIDCOT) - OXFORD

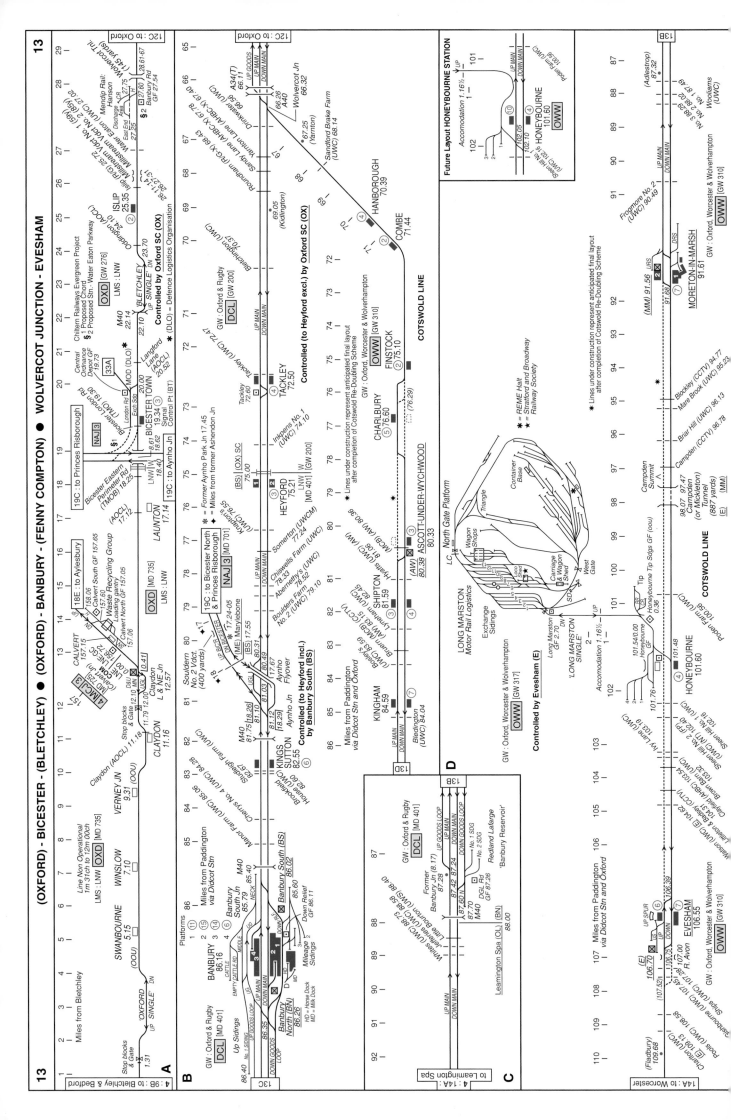

PERSHORE - WORCESTER - DROITWICH SPA & SHELWICK JUNCTION ● WOOTTON BASSETT - WESTERLEIGH JUNCTION

A

13D : to Evesham

COTSWOLD LINE

Miles from Paddington via Didcot Station & Oxford

15B : to Stoke Works Jn and Bromsgrove

GW : Oxford, Worcester & Wolverhampton

PERSHORE 112.52 [GW 310] OWW

Mare's (UWC)(NJ) 112.06 ⑥

Coles (UWC) 114.56

Lewis No. 1 (UWC)(NJ) 113.48

Lewis No. 2 (UWC)(NJ) 113.31

114.67 (Stoulton)

LMS : Midland [GW 400] BAGI 2

15B : to Bromsgrove

68.15

116.66 / 68.38 / 68.60 / 68.74

Abbotswood Jn

Sadler's (UWC) 117.07

Norton Jn (NJ) 117.26

Cooksholme (UWC) 0.25

ABW [GW 300]

15B : to Cheltenham Spa

LMS : Midland [GW 400] BAGI 2

Controlled by Gloucester SC (G)

M5 118.04

Crown Packaging Covered Loading Dock

North Sidings GF 120.17

Wyld's Lane Jn 120.14

North Sidings

Hereford Sdgs GF 120.38

WORCESTER SHRUB HILL 120.42 (SH) 120.31

GW & LMS (Mid) Joint

Platforms: 1a ⑤, 1b ⑦, 2 ⑬, 3 ③

Barrow (WL) 120.47

Shrub Hill Jn 120.46

WAH [GW 340]

GW : Worcester & Hereford

120.64 (Rainbow Hill Jn)

Worcester Tunnel Jn (TJ) 120.72

Rainbow Hill Tunnel (212 yards) 121.09-120.79

Worcester Tunnel Jn

BLW [GW 350]

GW : Worcester & Hereford

Worcester Viaduct (935 yards) 122.09

Worcester River Severn 121.12

WORCESTER FOREGATE STREET 121.12 ⑦

0.30

Henwick (HK) 121.71

OWW [GW 300]

123.10 (Fernhill Heath)

14B WAH [GW 340]

GW : Worcester & Hereford

DROITWICH SPA 126.10 ⑥ [GW 300]

OWW [GW 370]

GW : Oxford, Worcester & Wolverhampton

Clawson Footpath 125.24

OWW [GW 400]

GW : Oxford, Worcester & Wolverhampton

129.40 (Cutnall Green)

STO [GW 300]

127.76

Droitwich Spa Jn 126.21

126.59

(DS) 126.26

4 : 20C : to Kidderminster

B

1A

123.68-65

River Teme Viaduct (70 yards)

Newland East 126.22 (NE) ⊠

GREAT MALVERN 129.06 ⑦

MALVERN LINK 127.75 ⑥ ⑨

Malvern Wells 130.13 (MW) ⊠

129.59

ENGRS SDGS 130.18

Colwall (New) Tunnel (1586 yards) 130.48

COLWALL 131.72 ⑤ 131.40

Ledbury Tunnel (1316 yards) 135.75-15

LEDBURY 136.09 ⑤

(L) 136.06 ⊠

Ledbury Viaduct (372 yards) 136.56 / 136.39 / 136.30

Miles from Paddington via Didcot Station & Oxford

WORCESTER & HEREFORD SINGLE

SHL [GW 730]

27B : to Craven Arms

Shelwick Green (UWC) 147.48

Rimmel's (UWC) 143.34

Stoke Edith (AHBC) 142.32

(Withington) 145.36

Shelwick Jn 148.11

Controlled by Hereford (H)

27B : to Hereford

SHL [GW 730]

49.26

C

4B : to Swindon

Wootton Bassett West 84.07

84.50 / 84.07

E / W / M4

(Brinkworth) 87.01

Somerford Viaduct (150 yards)

89.62 (Little Somerford)

River Avon 90.29-22

UP BADMINTON / DOWN BADMINTON

93.70 / 94.21 (Hullavington) / 94.28

94.40 / 94.62

(B) SC / (SN) SC

Controlled by Swindon SC (SN)

Controlled by Bristol SC (B)

Miles from Paddington

Alderton WILD 98.30

GW SWB [GW 600]

(BADMINTON) 100.01

Alderton Tunnel (506 yards) 97.57-34

UP BADMINTON / DOWN BADMINTON 101.06

Chipping Sodbury Tunnel (2 miles, 926 yards)

103.48

Chipping Sodbury East GF 104.31

104.15 / 104.60 / 104.63

Chipping Sodbury Yard

YAT [GW 400]

(Wapley Common) 106.01

UP CHARF'D / DN CHARF'D 107.14

Westerleigh Jn 107.19/107.14

16B : to Yate & Gloucester

BGL2 [GW 400]

121.15

16B : to Bristol Parkway

16B

✦ = Switch Diamonds

August 2010

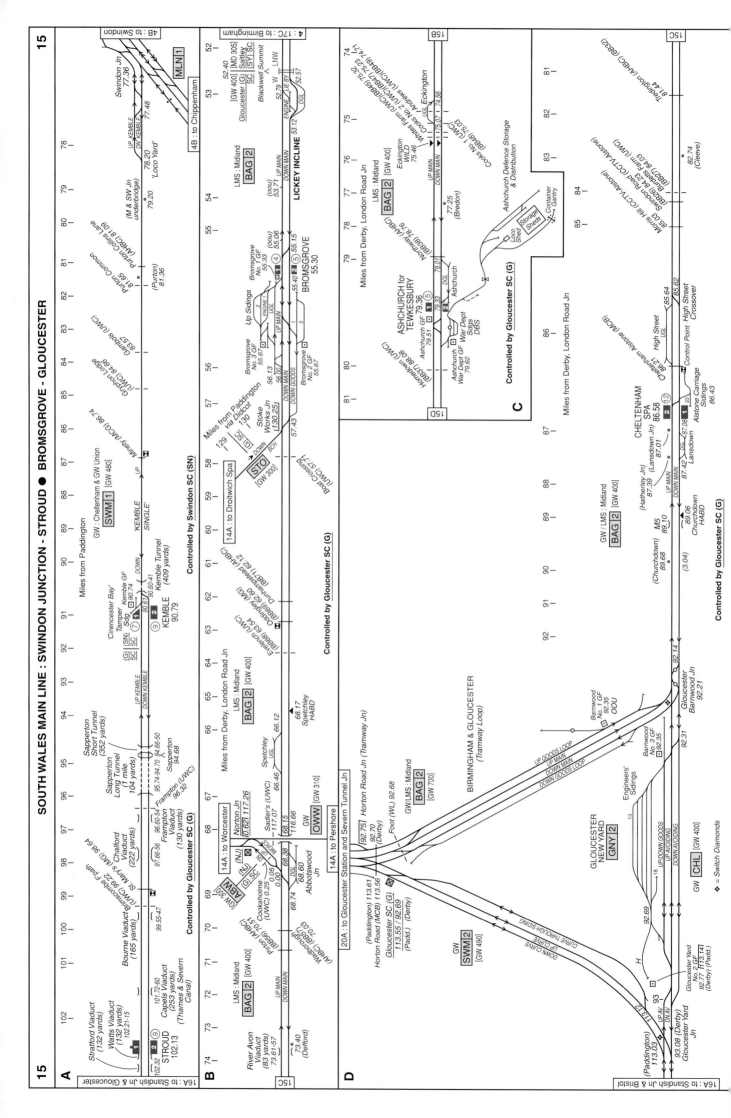

16 | 16

GLOUCESTER - BRISTOL (LAWRENCE HILL) ● SHARPNESS, TYTHERINGTON, WESTERLEIGH & AVONSIDE BRANCHES ● FILTON - SEVERN TUNNEL

August 2010

A

LMS : Midland 2 BGL 1 [GW 400]
COM
94.60 94.10
Gloucester Yard Jn
93.08
113.03
15D

94.74 Tuffley

Miles from Derby London Road Jn via Cheltenham and former Gloucester Eastgate

UP CHARFIELD
DOWN CHARFIELD

112

(Quedgley) 96.45

Lines to Berkeley Road Jn (incl.) & Kemble (exclusive) controlled by Gloucester SC (G)

97.02 (109.60)
(Naas, later Brookthorpe Crossing) Suppressed

111

Brookthorpe HABD 97.58
97.44 M5
98.16 UGL

Miles from Paddington via Swindon & Kemble

110

Haresfield

Haresfield Footpath (R/G) (BB16) 98.62

109

Standish Junction 99.20
99.69 (Derby)
106.74 (Padd.)

UP KEMBLE DOWN KEMBLE
102.11-07
102.27 (VL)
10.17
Old Ends (CCTV)

108

107

STONEHOUSE 104.74
Stonehouse Viaduct (90 yards)

SWM 1 [GW 480]
GW : Cheltenham & GW Union

106 105 104

Ebley (UWC) 103.49
103.11
103.09

Carpenters Viaduct (46 yards)

CAM & DURSLEY 105.30
M5 105.70
105.36 Coaley GF

LMS : Midland BGL 2 [GW 400]

15A : to Avonmouth
17A : to Stroud and Swindon

103 102 101 100 99 98 97 96 95 94

Berkley Road Jn
Berkeley 'SHARPNESS' SINGLE
BNFL (Magnox)
107.70 Gloucester SC (G)
Bristol SC (B)
0.04
M5 110.46

GW & LMS (Mid) Joint
SSS SAW [GW 425]
Severn & Wye Joint

Sharpness BW / MR
4.53 3.69
4.15 4.08 3.45
Lydney (See 20B)
former Severn Bridge

BW = British Waterways

Gate 13 (See note →)
Swing Bridge
Dock

Berkeley GF 2.08
Great Western Way
A to B approx 1 mile

UGL DGL
Charfield 112.72
113.08
112.56
Charfield Hall Farm 113.77
(UWC)(BB4)

Lawrence Hill GF
128.75/1.19
129.38
129.49
Barrow (or Day's) Road
Bristol City Council - GW Refuse Transfer Station
BAW [GW 456] LMS / BR

16B 16

B

20B : to Severn Tunnel Jn

Sudbrook Shaft 13.55

Severn Tunnel (4 miles 628 yards)

Controlled by South Wales Control Centre (SWCC) (NT), Severn Tunnel Workstation
from 6m 50ch (Dn Tnl.) and 8m 60ch (Up Tnl.)

Ableton Lane Tunnel (97 yards) 10.18
M49 over M4 over
10.51-55
A403 11.01
10.47
DN PILNING LOOP 10.15
UP PILNING LOOP

BSW [GW 900]
GW : Bristol & S Wales Union

PILNING 9.43
2 1 6

9.13
DN TUNNEL UP TUNNEL
9.08 Pilning HABD (NT)

on different levels
7.56

Patchway New Tunnel (1 mile) (M5)
Patchway Short Tunnel (62 yards) 7.53-56
Patchway Old Tunnel (1246 yards) 6.68 7.45
6.56
(B) (NT)

Miles from Bristol (Temple Meads)

10 11 12 13 14

PATCHWAY
5.77 5.61 [112.68]
Patchway Jn No.1 [112.72]
Patchway Jn No.2
0.00 : 5.53

SWB [GW 600]

Filton West Jn No.2 [5.41] 112.78
Filton West Jn No.1 112.72 [0.40]

Filton Tip (AOCL) 0.34
PCH [GW 5401]
(BR) (Padd.)

Stoke Gifford Jn No.2 —112
Stoke Gifford Jn No.1 111.79 (Filton)
111.77 Bristol Road
111.73 Stoke Gifford West Jn

BRISTOL PARKWAY 111.62
Platforms 2, 3 4
13 14

Miles from Paddington

108 109 110 111

111.38
111.24 Stoke Gifford East Jn
UPL
DOWN BADMINTON
UP BADMTN

(110.63 (Winterbourne)
(110.42-110.36

Winterbourne Viaduct (269 yards)
M4 Viaduct (139 yards)

Hackford Viaduct (Upford) (269 yards)
Coalpit Heath HABD's 109.27
(109.68 (Winterbourne)
(109.64-52

Bristol Road Viaduct (95 yards)
Broad Ln (UWC) 121.32
(NT) Westerleigh 107.14
DOWN CHARFIELD
UP CHARFIELD

Miles from Derby London Road Junction via Cheltenham and former Gloucester Eastgate

114 115 116 117 118 119

TYTHERINGTON
Tytherington Tunnel (224 yards)
5.46 5.56
Wickwar Tunnel (1401 yards)

TYTHERINGTON SINGLE

Grovesend Quarry Hanson Aggregates
A38
Loader OUTGOING INCOMING
Former line to Thornbury (Track lifted)

16A

LMS : Midland THO [GW 430]

Iron Acton Station
(AOCL) 4.66 Acton By-pass
Latteridge (TMO) 2.09 (TMO) 2.47

Yate South Jn 120.03
YATE 119.57 Yate Middle Jn 119.60
119.74 4 1 2
YAT [GW 400]
121.15
121.28
107 : to Swindon
DN BAD. 107.19 107.14

LMS : Midland BGL 2 [GW 440]

WESTERLEIGH
Railfreight Terminal
South Gloucestershire Council Refuse Transfer Station 122.40
Murco Oil Terminal 122.22
Gantry 122.34
Engineers Training School
Engineer's Sidings 122.20
Broad Ln (UWC) 121.32
OTM 122.65
YD1 YD2 STOPBLOCK ROAD
M4 Compound

Controlled by Bristol SC (B)

FILTON ABBEY WOOD
Filton Jn 4.36 Bristol Road
4.50 (Filton)
4.40 DF
4.30
4.08 Filton South Jn

FILTON
HABD 4.75
BSW [GW 451]
FEC [GW 450]

FILTON [GW 4501]
AFR [GW 4501]
Recycling Depot

AVONMOUTH
DOWN 5.22 BRISTOL
UP FILTON
DOWN FILTON
DOWN REC
UP SPUR
PLAT 4 LINE
DGL

Stoke Gifford No.1 DBS
Stoke Gifford Down Sdgs
111.69 Barrow (WL)
111.20
Sdgs 'Light'
5 4 3 2 1

HORFIELD 3.55
[GW 450]

UB = Up Bristol
DB = Down Bristol
UF = Up Filton
DF = Down Filton

Cheltenham Road Viaduct (145 yards)
MONTPELIER 2.68
Montpelier Tunnel (288 yards)
2.61-47
CNX [GW 454]
3.09-03
'AVONMOUTH SINGLE'
6 10 1 2

Midland Railway overbridge (Ashley Hill)
2.42
2.06 Narroways Hill Jn
2.03
M32 1.62
1.56-1.58 Stapleton Road Viaduct
STAPLETON ROAD 1.50

DOWN FILTON
UP FILTON

LAWRENCE HILL 1.04
0.71
(Dr. Days Jn)
Gantry

to Bristol Temple Meads
to North Somerset Jn
5B : to North Somerset Jn

© Copyright TRACKmaps. No reproduction without permission

16 16

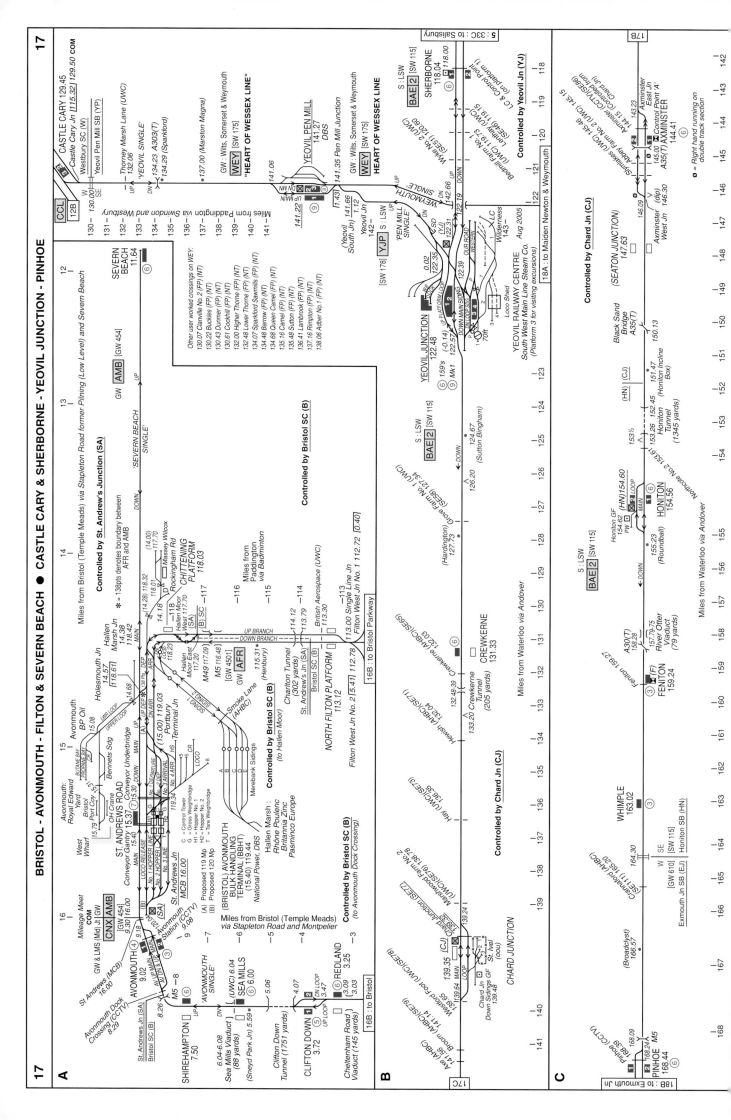

(YEOVIL PEN MILL) - (DORCHESTER) ● EXMOUTH BRANCH ● CHILTERN LINE : LONDON MARYLEBONE - AYLESBURY - (CLAYDON)

August 2010

Panel A / B (Exmouth Branch)

17C : to Honiton

S : LSW BAE 2 (GW 610)

East Sidings (oou)

170   169

Miles from Waterloo via Andover

Exmouth Junction

WATERLOO UP 170.20
WATERLOO DOWN
SIDING
ARRIVAL

Exmouth Jn (EJ) 170.21 / 0.00

West Sidings (oou)

EMT (GW 611)

THE AVOCET LINE

Exmouth Jn 170.27 / -0.01
POLSLOE BRIDGE 0.34
SINGLE
EXMOUTH

DIGBY & SOWTON 2.20
S : LSW
A379 (2.46)

TOPSHAM Topsham (CCTV) 4.23 3.28
4.34

(River Clyst Viaduct (114 yards))
5.39 Water Lane (UWC)
5.51 Daws Lane (UWC)
EXTON 5.67
LYMPSTONE COMMANDO 6.23
Sea Wall 5.57
LYMPSTONE VILLAGE 7.28
7.17
7.71
Sea Wall 8.18 8.38 8.68

EXMOUTH 9.32

Branch controlled by Exmouth Junction (EJ)

ST. JAMES' PARK 170.72

Blackboy Tunnel (262 yards)
170.43 170.44 170.56

171

7A : to Exeter

17B : to Yeovil Pen Mill

To Yeovil Junction

17B : to Sherborne 122.19

142.66

Other user worked crossings on WEY:
143.36 Bradford Abbas (FP) (NT)
147.68 Bubdown Lane (FP) (NT)
148.60 Melbury Bubb Down Farm (FP) (NT)
148.60 Woolcombe Bank (FP) (NT)

THORNFORD 144.35
YETMINSTER 145.46
Thornford Bridge Crossing (UWC) 144.24
Bere Hackett (UWC) 145.63
CHETNOLE 147.50
Meads Farm (UWC) 146.16
Mill Farm (UWC) 145.70

Miles from Paddington via Swindon and Westbury

MAIDEN NEWTON 154.12

Dorchester South (DR) 153.19 154.02

GW : Wilts, Somerset & Weymouth

Cattistock
(Cattistock)

Pound Lane (UWC) 147.10
Evershot Tunnel (308 yards) 149.63-149.49
Evershot 149.77
Bull Farm (NT) 150.00
Frome Tunnel 151.16
WEYMOUTH SINGLE 150.20

HEART OF WESSEX LINE

SOUTH EASTERN TERRITORY

North London Line to Gospel Oak

WEY (SW 175)

Bradford Peverell Viaduct (66 yards)
159.29-26
Poundbury Viaduct 160.63-61 160.31-28 161
Chick Farm (Station) 158.88
R. Frome Viaduct
Stratton (Grimstone & Frampton) Tunnel (651 yards)
Grimstone & Frampton 157.47-46 157.57
Hyde (UWC) 155.78 Crockway (UWC) 157.19 Crockway (UWC) 155.03
5 : 31D : to Dorchester & Weymouth

Panel C / D (Chiltern / Marylebone)

Platforms
1 ①
2, 3 ① ⑫
4 ⑤
5 ⑥
6 ①

IECC (ME) 205.77
LONDON MARYLEBONE 205.77
WALL SIDING

Regent's Canal 205.42 205.48
UP SDG 205.44 205.33

Miles from Manchester (London Road) line via former GCR line

London Underground distances, in kilometres from former Ongar Station

205.22 TUNNEL SDGS
St. John's Wood Tunnel (1606 yards)

To Euston LEC 1 204.40 204.37
2 : 1A, 4 : 1 2.29 To Willesden Junction
MCJ 1 [MD 701] LNE : GC

All NR lines from / to Marylebone controlled by Marylebone ASC (ME)
LUL Metropolitan and Jubilee lines controlled from Baker Street Signalling and Control Centre
(Jubilee Lines to be controlled from Neasden Signalling Centre from late 2010)

5 : 42B : LU to Baker St.

FINCHLEY ROAD 50.14 km
WEST HAMPSTEAD 50.75 km
Hampstead Tunnel (694 yards) 204.03 204.35
Canfield Place 204.00

KILBURN 51.84 km
WILLESDEN GREEN (JE) 53.03 km
Kilburn Viaduct 203.32 203.21 203.09
202.17 203.51 203.79

CAW [EA 1360] LMS : Mid
DOLLIS HILL 54.24 km
NJN [MD 715] LNE : GC
Territory Bdy on NJ

201.09
Neasden Junction (NJ) 16.56 / 7.03
LNW
6.51

NEASDEN (MM/JM) 55.09 km 200.76

2 : 1A, 4 : 1, 5 : 1 To Willesden Junction
5 : 41C London Underground Metropolitan Line to Watford
BOK 3

2 : 1A, 4 : 1, 5 : 1 To Action Wells Junction

London Underground Neasden Depot

METROPOLITAN SB
JUBILEE LINE SB
JUBILEE LINE NB
MET./NB
UP HARROW 200.66
DOWN HARROW
Neasden SB 6.24
Neasden South Sdgs
Bardon Aggregates
Tibbett & Britten

19A : to South Ruislip

M25 18.60 76.63 km (19.53)
CHORLEYWOOD 78.03 km
LU METROPOLITAN Line SB
LU METROPOLITAN Line NB (18.53)

Miles from Manchester (London Road) via former GC main line

161 160 159 158

To Cricklewood 201

WEMBLEY PARK 200 6m 59ch 57.38 km (MG)
Baker Street
MET SB LOCAL
NB SB LOCAL
WEMBLEY Park Sdgs
To Neasden Depot
UNDER
SB DEPOT

PRESTON ROAD 58.84 km 199
NORTHWICK PARK 60.49 km 198
MET NB LOCAL
NB MN LOCAL
SB LOCAL JUBILEE LINE
DOWN MAIN
UP MAIN

2 MCJ 1 COM MCJ 1 : GC LNE : GC 197.05
HARROW-ON-THE-HILL 61.78 km (9.39) 9.13
Harrow South Jn (199.41)
SB MAIN
NB MAIN
UP HARROW FAST
MET SB FAST

MCJ 1 [MD 701] LNE : GC

To Euston
West Coast Mainline (6 tracks)

LU Metropolitan Line to Uxbridge
9.18 LU Harrow (limit of electrification from the west)
(JB, subsidiaries & JF)
JB North LNW 197.62
JB

NORTH HARROW 63.77 km (10.57)
PINNER 65.25 km (11.52)
Harrow 10.08 North Jn 11

NORTHWOOD HILLS 67.33 km (12.76)
NORTHWOOD 68.95 km (13.78)
MOOR PARK 71.16 km (15.28)

Spur Road
River Gade
Watford North Curve
Watford North Jn 16.28 72.77 km
Watford South Jn 16.45
Watford East Jn 16.57 73.10 km 73.35 km
South Sdgs
JP JJ 73.74 km
JP (17.36) North Sdgs

RICKMANSWORTH 74.52 km

JUBILEE LINE
GREAT MISSENDEN 29.00
WENDOVER 33.43
STOKE MANDEVILLE 35.75
PRA [MD 720]

Miles from Baker Street (Metropolitan)

All NR lines controlled by Marylebone ASC (ME) to 197.05

2 MCJ 1 [MD 710] LNE : GC
MCJ 2 [MD 712]

LT (Metropolitan) and LNE : GC Joint

AYLESBURY 38.08 38.13
Carriage Sidings
Aylesbury Jn
Chiltern Railways Maintenance Depot (AL)
Aylesbury Servicing Depot
CET 38.21 38.38 38.43
Underframe Cleaning Shop
Platforms 1 ① 2, 3 ⑨
Aylesbury North Goods Loop
37.62 49.35 49
[MD 725] [MD 710]
48 GW & LNE (GC) Jt

19B

Aylesbury Vale Jn 40.26 40.38 ⑧
AYLESBURY VALE PARKWAY
Aylesbury Vale
SINGLE 39.01
[MD 712]

QUAINTON ROAD 44.22
(Buckinghamshire Railway Centre see 32B)
GW : GC LNE : GC Jt
161.50 161.60
(Grendon Underwood Jn)
Ditchburns (UWC) 159.33
159.10 (Quinton Road Jn)

2 MCJ 2 COM
3 MCJ 2

13A : to Claydon L & NE Jn

Miles from Baker Street (Metropolitan Line)

AMERSHAM 84.85 km (23.70)
CHALFONT AND LATIMER 81.58 km (21.67)
London Underground Metropolitan Line to Chesham
LU : km from former Ongar Station
Mantles Wood Network Rail / LU Boundary 25.21 (87.08 km)
Altitude c500 feet 500ft

METROPOLITAN
SB NB
DOWN MAIN
UP MAIN

18D

© Copyright **TRACK**maps. No reproduction without permission

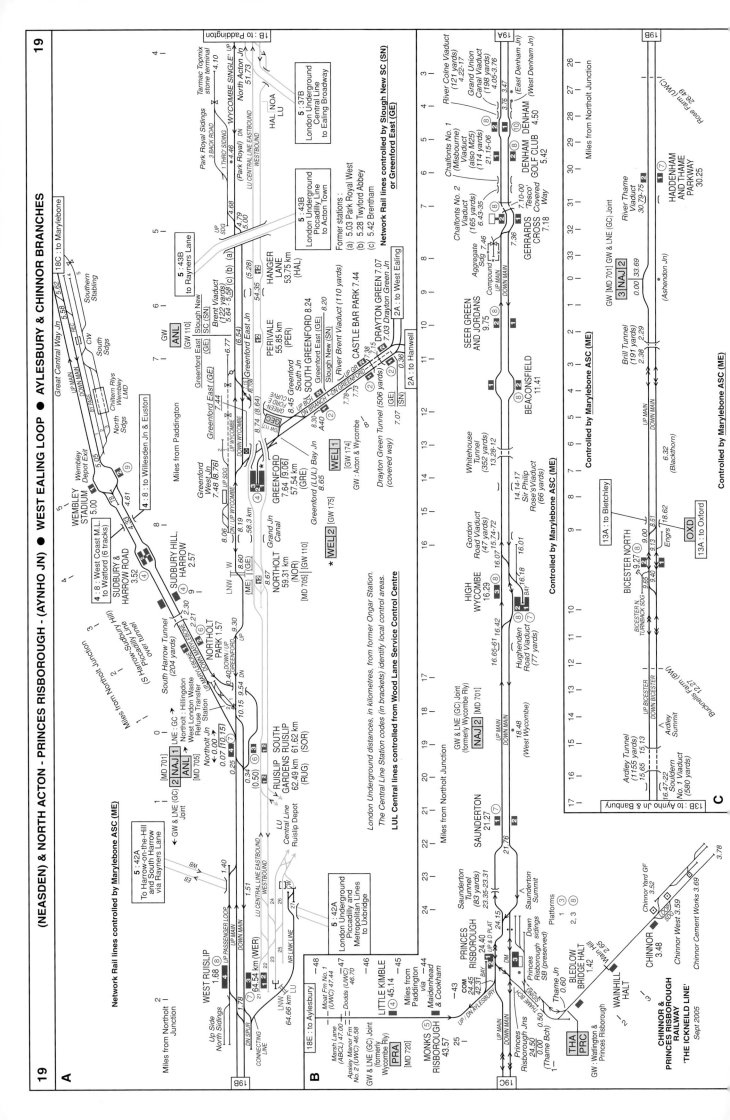

A

Miles from Paddington via Stroud

114 115 116 117 118 119 120 121 122 123 124 125 126 127 128 129 130 131 132

Controlled by Gloucester SC (G)

15D : to Bristol & Cheltenham

Gloucester Horton Road
On-track Plant Depot
No. 2 SPUR
No. 1 SPUR
PARCELS LINE
C = Calibration Sidings
92.75 LC
LOOP
113.61 / 60
113.67 Foot (WL) Horton Road Jn (Tramway Jn)

Gloucester Old Yard
North End ⑫
South End ⑫
GLOUCESTER 114.04
Post Office Bank
SOUTHBY ③

114.01
Carriage Sidings ⑯
UP RELIEF
UP MAIN
DOWN MAIN
Barrow (WL) 114.19
Gloucester Viaduct (345 yards)
St Catherine's Meadow Viaduct (84 yards)
Gloucester West
114.36-114.20
Over Jn
115.24-16 115.04-00
Ham Meadow Viaduct (172 yards)
115.43
UP MAIN
DOWN MAIN

GW : Gloucester & Forest of Dean [GW 700] SWM 2
Keen's 116.02 (GS71)
Poole's (UWC) 116.46 (GS72)
Lower Barn Farm 118.17 (UWC)
Ley Crossing Farm No. 1 (UWC) 120.76 (GST10) 120.20
Broken Cross Farm No. 2 (UWC) 120.66 (GST13)
Grange Court 121.32 D
Grange Court GF 121.28
121.48 F
121.02
121.75 UGL (GS72)
DGL
Westbury (AHBC) 121.11 (GS16)
Newnham Tunnel (235 yards)
Bradeak 123.36 123.37
Ruddle Bridge (UWC) 125.22 (GST22)
125.19-08
Bullo Pill HABD 125.59
Bullo Dock Viaduct (40 yards)
126.40-38
UP MAIN
DOWN MAIN

Aldridge Crossing (UWC) 130.65 (QW)
Awre (CCTV) 138.22 (GS29)
132.32

Gloucester SC (G)
Newport SC (N)

20B

B

DEAN FOREST RAILWAY

12.42
Yorkley Rd (TMO) 12.32
PARKEND 12.25
D

NORCHARD
High Level/Low Level
Norchard 9.56
Restoration Shed
9.58
BB
LC (foot)
D
Middle Forge Jn
9.33
DOWN
9.64
9.65

Whitecroft 11.22
(Whitecroft)
11.25
B42.34 (TMO)
10.60 (Tufts Jn)
Garlands No. 1 133.72

12
11
10
9
8

TIDENHAM
1.13
-1
0.73
Wye Valley Jn GF (oou)
140.52 / 0.00
GW : Wye Valley [GW 704] WYE
Line Out of Use
0.66
DN

GW : Glos & Forest of Dean [GW 700] SWM 2

D

DEAN FOREST RAILWAY

Miles from Berkeley Road Jn via Severn Bridge & Lydney Jn

A48 (TMO) 8.96
LYDNEY TOWN 8.74
ST. MARY'S HALT 8.41
Lydney Bypass (ABCL) 8.34

20B

CAERWENT BRANCH

To CAERWENT
Defence Rail and Container Services CWT
The entire branch is private

33B

M48 1.34
1.63 AV
← DOWN
0.28
Caerwent Branch GF
Caerwent Branch Jn 146.76 (Portskewett) 0.00
147.02
147.04

1
15
⑤ (UWC) 15.58 15.29
SBK 1 (GW 705)
SBK 2
Caldicot HABD 146.00 / -145.67
Iron Hill Farm 145.50
Curb Hut (UWC) 145.11
Three Gates (UWC) 144.06 (GST53) (GST54) 143.15
Sea Wall
Severn Tunnel (4 miles 628 yards)
142.21 141.68
143.04 M48
Sudbrook Shaft
Sudbrook Pumping Station 0.73
SUDBROOK 13.55

BSW GW : Severn Tunnel [GW 900]

Post Office No. 1 (TMO) 146.65 / 0.40
Post Office No. 2 (TMO) 0.60
CALDICOT 148.02
Caldicot (MCB) 147.05 (GST65)
147
148
148.00
148.36
⑤ (UWC)

CWO
Pulp Mills (TMO)

16B : to Bristol

Severn Tunnel area

149

[CYFFORDD TWNEL HAFREN] 16
SEVERN TUNNEL JUNCTION
S.T. Jn Interlocking
UP TNL LOOP
DOWN TUNNEL
UP TUNNEL
(NT) (N)
UP MAIN 2
DOWN RELIEF ⑦
16.39
148.36
Severn Tunnel Jn
BSW SWM 2 [GW 900] [GW 700]
GW : South Wales
16.73 149.14
149.24
149.47
M4 149.46 (W)
OTM Calibration Tank
CR
Gator Garage
UP MAIN
DOWN MAIN
DR (E)
[GW 900] SWM 2

20C

21A : to Newport

Lines in the Severn Tunnel Jn area
Controlled by South Wales Control Centre (SWCC) (NT), Severn Tunnel Workstation

Lydney area

20D

Lydney Bypass (ABCL) 8.34
Harbour Road (MCB) 8.19
8.24
8.20
Naas (AHBC) (GST36)
Lydney GF 8.00
132.71
133.21
133.32
Lydney (MCB) 132.60
LYDNEY 133.37
132.40
UGL
DGL
GW & LMS (Mid) Severn & Wye Jt
SAW
LYDNEY JUNCTION (Dean Forest Rly)
8.12
NR
⑤ ④
133.20
Miles from Berkeley Road Jn via Severn Bridge (See 16A)

12
132
133
134
135
136
137
138
139
140
141
142
143
144
145
146
147
148

Miles from Paddington via Stroud

GW : South Wales SWM 2 [GW 700]

CHEPSTOW [CAS-GWENT] 141.33
River Wye Chepstow River Bridge (200 yards) 141.15-141.05
Chepstow (or Tutshill) Tunnel (359 yards) 140.75-140.59
Woolaston (RG) 136.71 135.04
Hardacre No. 2 (UWC) 135.14
High Hall (UWC) 133.72
138.14
⑤ 2 1

UP MAIN
DOWN MAIN

C

Controlled by Newport SC (N)

150 151 152 153 154 155 156

UP RELIEF
UP RELIEF
UP MAIN
DOWN MAIN
DOWN RELIEF
(Undy)
151.05
•150.50
151.02
Magor Crossovers
Bishton Flyover Bridge (200 yards)
152.30
Bishton (MCB) 153.01 (GCE)
153.20 (NT) (EWWn) (STWn) (NT)
Llanwern Works East Connection 153.05
Slab Unloading
(to back of works)

Coil Unloading
WB
Exchange Sidings
Repairs
LLANWERN WORKS
Corus Strip Products Division
(Site of LLANWERN) 154.66
UP SERVICE LINE
DOWN SERVICE LINE

Bishton HABD's 155.07
Llanwern West Jn 156.11
Llanwern Works West Connection 156.03

Miles from Paddington via Stroud

GW : South Wales SWM 2 [GW 900]
[GW 710]

UP MAIN
UP RELIEF
DOWN MAIN
DOWN RELIEF

20B

Lines from Patchway 6.50 (Down Tunnel) and 8.60 (Up Tunnel) also Caldicot Station 148.10 to Llanwern East 153.20
Controlled by South Wales Control Centre (SWCC) (NT), Severn Tunnel Workstation

Lines from Llanwern East 153.20 to East Usk Jn 157.20 (including the East end of Usk Jn Yard and the Uskmouth branch)
Controlled by South Wales Control Centre (SWCC) (NT), East Usk Workstation

20

August 2010

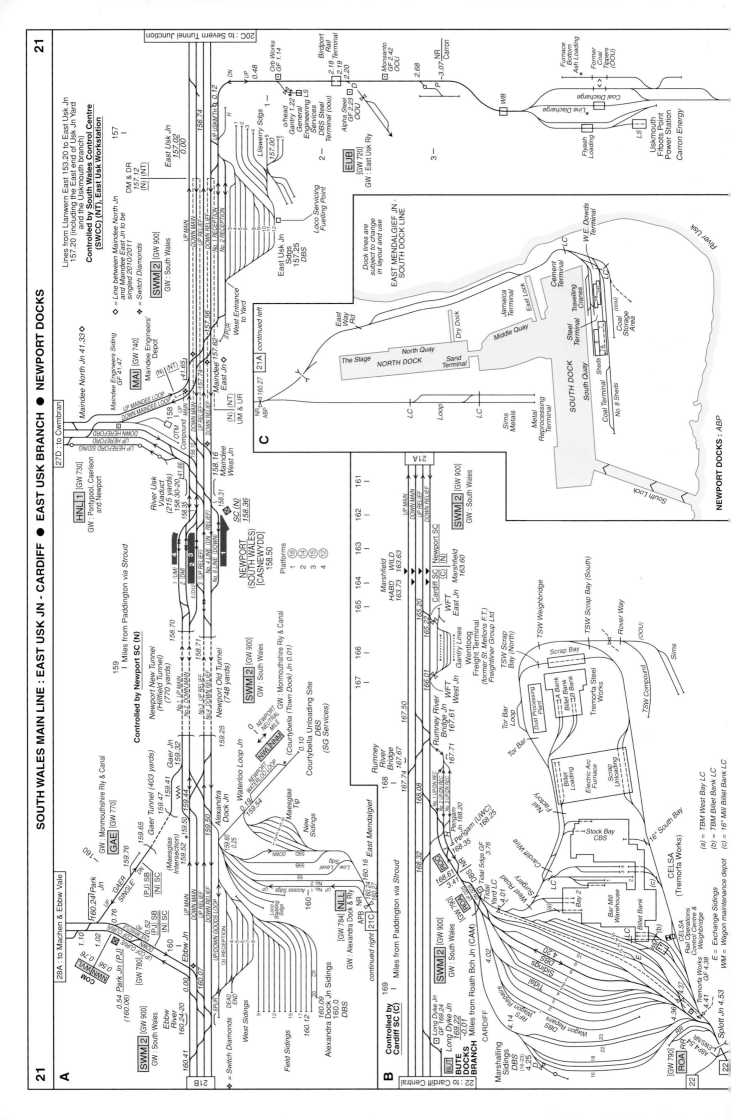

South Wales Main Line / Cardiff Bay and Penarth Branches / Cardiff Docks

Miles from Paddington via Stroud

Controlled by Cardiff SC (C)

21B : to Newport

169

21B : to Newport

SWM 2 [GW 900] GW : South Wales

NIRU □ Long Dyke GF 169.24
0.19 Long Dyke Jn 169.22
Windsor -0.01
Rd 0.25
NR
CELSA 0.33
NR/

CELSA (Castle Works)

CELSA (Castle Works)

CRM Billet Bank (South)

Parson's Corner

David's Road

WB

CRM Coil Bays

Billet

Bar Bays

Coil Bays

Dock Sidings

Former Bute East Dock (closed)

BUT [GW 8001]

No.3 LINE Queen Street South Jn
28B : to Merthyr & Rhymney
Newtown West 169.75
170.00 0.62

Pump House 5.19

STONEFIELD-SPLOTT JN LINE

Miles from Roath Branch Jn (CAM)

Ocean Splott 4.53
W Jn 4.54 DBS
ABP 0.65
Lewis Rd (NE Jn)
(South East Jn) 4.70
CELSA ABP 4.76
Clipper Rd 4.63
Timber Yd

CDK 1

CDK 2

European Metal Recycling

4.72
STONEFIELD LOOP 5.20
Ryan's Dowlais Wharf
Ryan's Hopper (OOC)
Compass Rd
5.26
Stone Locks Rd Loading
Cold Stores Rd 'A' 5.38
Cold Stores Rd 'B' 5.48
5.60 (Kings Jn)

(OOC) = Out of Commission

ROATH DOCK

Oil Dock

Pontoon Wharf Fletchers Wharf

CDK 2 4 3

CDK 3

DOCK STORAGE SOUTH - KINGS JN LINE

Empire Wharf

Kings Wharf

Bells Wharf

Communication passage • On Alex South Sdg • On Cawoods

(CCL Container Terminal)*

QUEEN ALEXANDRA DOCK

ROATH BRANCH Coastal Rd 5.77

Longships Rd 6.12

CARDIFF DOCKS Associated British Ports

(Mileage within Cardiff Docks provisional)

Swing Bridge

Britannia Quay

ROATH BASIN

Inner Lock

Oil Berth (Timber Terminal)*

Entrance Lock 6.13

HCB Energy Oil terminal

RIVER TAFF Channel Dry Dock

Outer Lock

Barrage

Cardiff Central / Canton

171 172 169 170 171

South Wales Signalling Centre (SWCC) ⊠ (NT) 170.61

BRICKYARD SDG

Leckwith Loop North Junction 171.55 0.00

Taff River Viaduct (122 yards) 170.42-38

Fish Dock Sdg
UP PLAT
PLAT 0
UP RELIEF 1 2
UP MAIN
DOWN MAIN
DOWN RELIEF 3 4
UP BY RLF 6 7
170.45 170.47 DOWN BARRY UP BARRY

CEJ 0.10
CEJ [GW 830] Cardiff East Jn 170.18/0.00
East Junction Viaduct (177 yards)

170.30 Cardiff Central [CAERDYDD CANOLOG] 170.30
Platforms 0 7 15 12
0 1-4 6,7
Riverside Sdg
Cardiff SC (C) 170.33

170.56 170.09 170.05 170.11 170.22 0.19
DOWN BARRY UP BARRY DOWN SINGLE UP

BUTE RD 'BUTE RD'

CAM [GW 839] GW : TV

CARDIFF BAY [BAE CAERDYDD] 0.02 4

No.2 UP RELIEF No.1 UP RELIEF UP RELIEF

0.10 (170.56) Cardiff Penarth Curve West Jn

Penarth Curve East No. 1 GF 0.23
Radyr Branch Jn 0.25
Penarth Curve East No. 2 GF 0.30

BRY [GW 830] GW : TV

CCD =
CCC =
CCS =

Canton TMD (Pullman Rail)

Washer PR Carriage Shed ATW
M M
S S
CARDIFF CANTON (CF)
DMU shed
DMU 4 (FUELLING)
DMU 5 (FUELLING)
FUELLING
Taff Vale Sdgs Canton Engrs' Sdgs

Leckwith Rd Bridge GF 171.26
HST SPUR

171.27 171.49

TB No.2 UP RELIEF No.1 UP RELIEF

Penarth Curve North Jn 0.25
* Penarth Curve North No. 1 GF 0.47 0.47
RAD [GW 830]

CPL 0.00
DOWN PENARTH CURVE UP PENARTH CURVE GW : TV [GW 860]

Penarth Curve South Jn 0.47

Penarth Harbour Jn 0.70

BRY [GW 830] GW : TV

* 5-10 = Exchange Sidings
§ 5-10 = Exchange Sidings

ATW : Arriva Trains Wales
PR : Pullman Rail
(Pullman Design and Fabrication Ltd.)

B = Old Water Tower
M = Maintenance Sheds - PR
S = Servicing Shed - PR
U = Underframe Cleaning (ATW)
W = Wheel Lathe (ATW)

SWM 2 [GW 900] GW : South Wales

23A : to Fairwater & Radyr

23A : to Bridgend

Leckwith Loop Jn South 0.26
NINIAN PARK [PARC NINIAN] 0.63 7

CLL [GW 850]
LECKWITH LOOP

RAD [GW 840] GW : TV

Penarth / Barry line

GRANGETOWN 0.73 6
BRY [GW 830]

Ely River Viaduct (66 yards) 1.46 1.49

Cogan Loops

Cogan Jn 2.29 5
COGAN 2.41 6
BRY [GW 830] GW : Barry

0.60 6

DINGLE ROAD [HEOL DINGLE] GW : TV

PTH [GW 864] GW : TV PENARTH 1.12

DOWN 0.01 6

Cogan Tunnel (220 yards) 2.75 3.05

30B : to Barry

© Copyright TRACKmaps. No reproduction without permission

August 2010

22 22

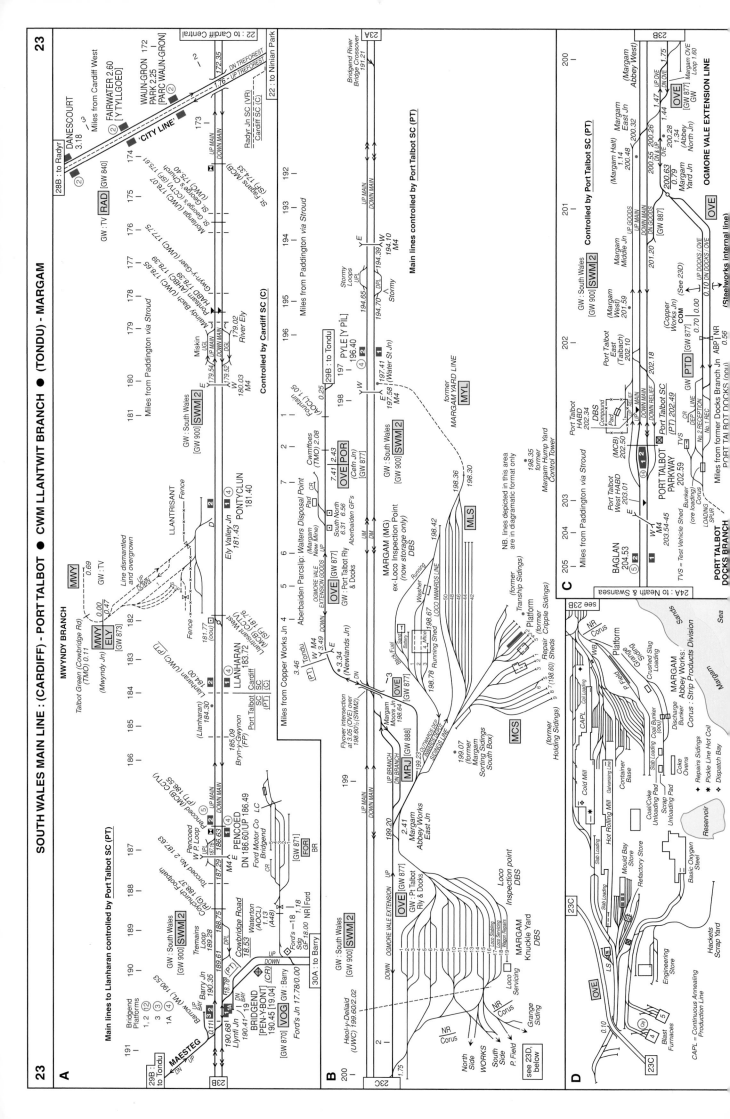

A

Controlled by Port Talbot SC (PT)

GW : South Wales SWM 2 [GW 900]

23C : to Port Talbot

Briton Ferry Briton Ferry East 205.36 East
Briton Ferry UP/DN THRO 205.29
Briton Ferry Up Flying Loop Jn 206.14 (17.39)
HABD 205.52
(Baglan Branch Jn) EM 4
Baglan Bay
W 7 0.36
Port Walleroo Crossing 206.01
A48(T)
BAN 205.76
BP Chemicals Ltd. (former Briton Ferry Dock)

Mileages in brackets are former R & SB
BRITON FERRY [LLANSAWEL]
206.40
206.52
UP FLYING LOOP (UP R & SB)
Up Sdgs
Down Sdgs
Briton Ferry Sidings

Court Sart Jn (Down) 206.58 (18.07)
Pennlwyn Crossing (UWC) 207.20
New Cut Vdct (68 yards) 207.36-39 (18.66-69)
Neath R. Vdct (Swing Bdg) 150 yards) 207.61-67
Pad : Neath Abbey Wharf Steel Supply
Dyneover GF 19.36
GW : R & SB RSB [GW 8901]
Miles from Treherbert via Blaenrhondda
207.57
207.78
UP RSB 19.16
DN RSB
M4 19.72
Jersey Marine Jn South

* R. Neath Viaduct (88 yards) 208.46-42 A465(T)

[GW 892] GW VON
A465(T) 43.05
Dynevor Jn 207.67
42.60 (PT) SC
LER [GW 894]
DOWN EM 4
JERSEY MARINE 41.26
W LOOP
SDI 1 [GW 890]
Miles from former Lonlas Jn at 1.07 on SWM 2

NEATH [CASTELL-NEDD] 208.20
208.26
24B 208.49
41.25
41.67
41.20
Neath & Brecon Jn 41.21
Neath Abbey Vdct (65 yds) 208.32-32
SDI 1
42
43.18
43.61
44
Jersey Marine Jn North 208.33
M4 208.31
UP SWANSEA DIST
DOWN SWANSEA DISTRICT 207.78
1.24
1.62
1.26
2.24
J [2.26]
20.07
20.24 Jersey Marine Jn South
M4 44.27
44.19 44.17
T P E
SWANSEA DOCKS

Controlled by Port Talbot SC (PT)
GW VON [GW 892]

J = from Jersey Marine North Jn
P = from Pontypool Road via Aberdare
T = from Treherbert via Blaenrhondda

B

ONLLWYN WASHERY & DISTRIBUTION CENTRE: Walters

Glyn Neath : Cwmgwrach: Ryans Disposal Point Wenallt, Lyn, Rheola and Pentreclwydau Mines (Cwm Nant Lleici Quarry)

32.77 Pad
32.62
33.08
VON [GW 892]
GW : Vale of Neath
33.14 (Aberpergwm Colliery Jn)
Aberpergwm
NR

MGR TRACK
Bunker
Coal Unloading
LC
Container Loading
Pre
Onllwyn GF 10.11
BAL
Walters
10.26 (old SB)
10.10 LC
NR

8.53 (Seven Sisters)
Ynisdawley Viaduct (51 yards)
8.25 8.23 Brynteg (UWC)
7.55 7.46 Nant-y-Cefn (UWC)
5.40 (Crynant)
5.03 Llwynllanc Fm (UWC) No. 1
Cefn Coed (UWC) 2.74 (Blaenant)
4.19 Tilfsat No. 1 (UWC) 2.52
3.75
Glyn-y-Mili (UWC)
1 UP SINGLE
35.25 (Resolven)
36.62 Ynysdwhant (UWC) (NT)
37.34 Clyne (TMO)
VALE OF NEATH
39.47 39.51
40
41
41.15
41.17 Neath & Brecon Jn
Miles from Pontypool Road via Aberdare
Aberdylais Vdct (75 yards) (R. Neath)
SINGLE
0.72# UP SINGLE
SD
0.01 DN
41.20 SD 41.21
NAB [GW 893]
GW : Neath & Brecon
SWM 2 208.49
Neath & Brecon Jn 41.21
24A
24

Miles from Paddington via Stroud

Landore Jn 214.57 214.62
SWM 2 [GW 900]
GW : South Wales
UP MAIN 214.39
DOWN MAIN
Landore Viaduct (389 yards)
Former Swansea Vale Rly; closed 2007
Cwm (path) 2.09
2.14 2.44
2.67 2.73
(Six Pit)
25A : to Bynea via
25A : to Llanelli via Bynea
LLANSAMLET 212.08
Lonlas Tnl (924 yards)
211.18-10
1.08
1.07 (Lonlas Jn) (Miles from former Skewen Jn on SWM 2)
SKEWEN [SCIWEN] 210.26
210.44 (Skewen Jn)
Skewen Vdct (29 yards) 209.70
Llandarcy GF 0.37
0.27 0.48
0.00 208.49
SDI 1
[GW 890]
2 SDI 1
THRO SDG
W
UP DISTRICT
DN DISTRICT

SWM 2 [GW 900]
GW : South Wales
Swansea Loop West Jn 215.14
Swansea Loop West Jn 0.00
25A : to Llanelli
215.46
Swansea Loop East Jn 215.42
LLY
= LLY
Landore (LE)
SWA [GW 9001]
GW : South Wales
UP SWANSEA AVOIDING LINE
SINGLE SWANSEA AVOIDING LINE
DOWN SWANSEA AVOIDING LINE
UP MAIN
DOWN MAIN
HST Sidings : FGW
FP
CW
Traction Maintenance Depot
FWGT 215.00
Maliphant Sidings (NIRU)
Maliphant Crossing (TMO) 215.42
Carriage Sidings i/c DBS
Appl-ication Apron 215.30 215.34
Down Sdgs GF 215.62
SWANSEA [ABERTAWE] 216.07
Rinse Apron 215.46
SWA [GW 9001]
GW
SWL [GW 906]
GW
SWANSEA LOOP
UP SWANSEA LOOP
DOWN SWANSEA LOOP
216

CARRIAGE WASHERS LINE
Down Sdgs
(OOU)
0.53
0.48

Miles from Pontypool Rd via Aberdare
46
Burrows Jn (King's Dock) 46.66 46.05
47
45
46.36
DOWN/UP DOCKS
AVOIDING
DOWN REC.
Swansea Burrows Sidings No. 1 Set
DBS
46.49
46.57
Burrows Jn 46.66
SKD
SWANSEA KING'S DOCK LINE
NR A482 (Fabians Way) 0.11
ABP
0.12
(King's Dock Jn)
(OOU)
SNK 3
DAN
DANYGRAIG BRANCH
(ex Ford Motor Co site, now Swansea Gate Business Park)
46.22

SWANSEA DOCKS
Associated British Ports (NCBO)

Container Berth Dragon Shipping
King's Dock North Side Lines
King's Dock South Side Lines
SNK 2
Coal Dump
No. 4 Quay
No. 6 Quay
No. 5 Quay
No. 7 Quay
No. 9 Quay
'E' Morrissey Cement
Deca Coal Plant
Rose Wharf
QUEEN'S DOCK
KING'S DOCK
Scherzer Passage
King's Lock
No. 3 Quay
No. 2 Quay
No. 1 Quay
Sand Wharves
Tennant's Wharf
D Shed
PRINCE OF WALES DOCK
1.19
G B A
N

August 2010

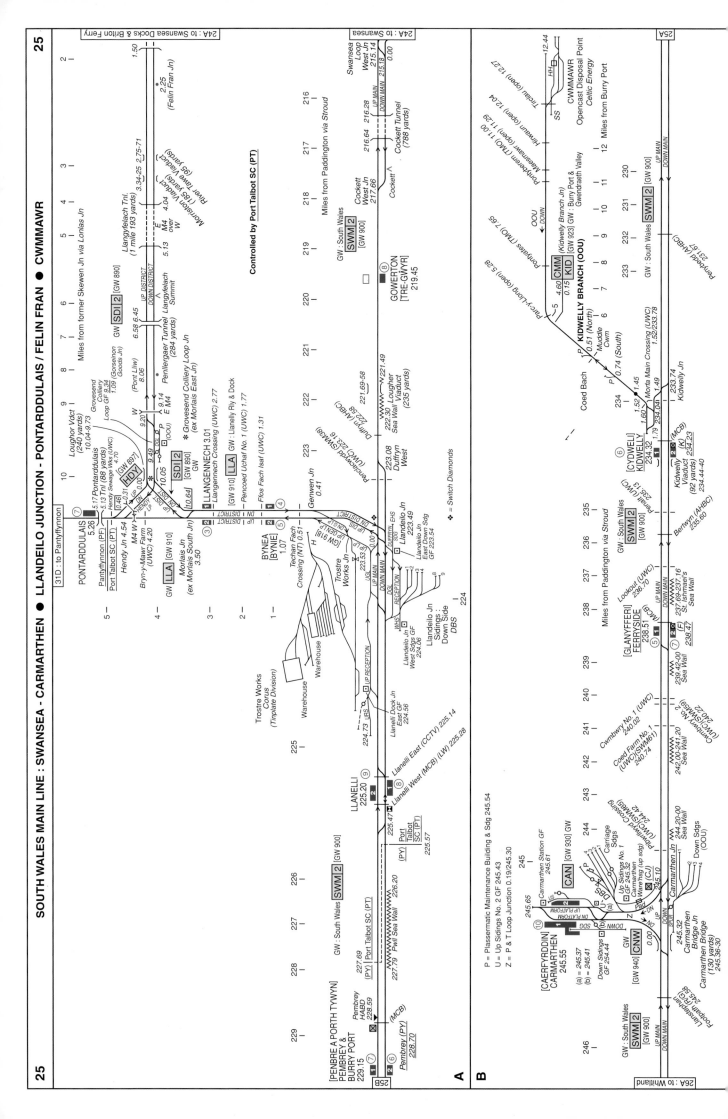

A

2B : to Carmarthen

Gwili (SWM67) 247.00
Nantyci No.2 (SWM68) 247.37
Gorsgoch (UWC)(CL) 249.57
Nantgaredig (UWC)(ALCC) 249.74
Sarnau Lower (SWM72) 249.11
Brady (UWC)(CL) 249.11
Sarnau (UWC)(CL) 252.45
Deri (SWM74) 252.45
St. Clears GF 253.08
St. Clears (CCTV) 253.18
Ffynnongain (R&G) 254.29

GW : South Wales [GW 900] SWM 2

Whitland Tunnel (187 yards) 257.10-01
Ffosdd (SWM83)(W) 258.02
Trewydd No.2 (SWM84) 258.49
Trewydd (UWC) 258.49
(MOB)(W) 258.68
[HENDY-GWYN] WHITLAND 258.74
Platforms 1, 2, 3
Down Sdgs GF 258.79
Whitland Jn 259.01
Llwyndyrys (UWC) 259.39
Llanboidy (AHBC) 259.54

Trewern Mill (UWC) 260.51
Llanmilwe Farm (UWC) 260.00
Trewern Farm (SWM89)(UWC) 260.64
Sambs (UWC) 260.74

Llwyndoys (UWC) 265.43

CLUNDERWEN 264.22
264.22

CLARBESTON ROAD 270.71
2B

Miles from Paddington via Stroud

GW : South Wales [GW 900] SWM 2

B

Clarbeston Road Jn SC (CR) 271.09
Clarbeston Road Jn 271.08

Miles from Paddington via Stroud

Spittal Tunnel (243 yards) 274.51 / 274.40

Shoals Hook Crossing (UWC) 275.13
Tanyard (UWC) 273.72
Crundale Mill (UWC) 274.07
Crundale (AHBC) 274.34

GW : South Wales [GW 900] SWM 2

All lines controlled by Clarbeston Road Jn SC (CR)

Barrow (WL) 276.13
[HWLFFORDD] HAVERFORDWEST 276.08
DM 2
276.18
THROUGH SDG 275.65
DBS

Haverfordwest Bridge (58 yards) (River Cleddau) 276.37-34

GW [GW 900] CRL
'FISHGUARD' SINGLE

Miles from Paddington via Stroud

TRECWN BRANCH (Private branch - OOU)
(Trecwn Jn) 281.47
Letterston Jn 281.58
TRECWN [GW 990]
2.15
283.70 / 283.10
NPF FAD LP/PR / LP/RR 0.00
NPF CRL COM 283.30 / 281.58
Letterston East GF 281.47
Letterston West GF 283.70
Hendrewen (UWC) 285.10
Winsel Crossing (UWC) 279.06

Harbour Station GF 288.10
[PORTHLADD ABERGWAUN] FISHGUARD HARBOUR
Fishguard Harbour Station (AOCL) 288.11
GW : North Pembroke & Fishguard [GW 900]
Passenger Berth
14
North GF 288.27
End of main line 288.36 / 288.18

[ABERDAUGLEDDAU] MILFORD HAVEN 284.65
South GF 284.69
284.71

Container Berth
289.06 / 289
North Breakwater

MIL [GW 960] GW : Milford Railway
MILFORD HAVEN Robeston Refinery Elf Oil

LPG
CRIPPLES

Little Harmiston (or Trunk Sdg Jn) 282.00
Gulf Oil Branch Jn 0.00
282.08
Little Harmiston (UWC) 0.10
'WATERSTON SINGLE' (TRUNK)
The Farm (UWC) 2.15
2.05
2.33
2.35
LC
ERB [GW 980]
Steynton Crossing (UWC) 283.21 / 283.12
Herbrandston Jn
LNG Plant Stone
Discharge Sdg
LS
2.34
'ROBESTON UP SINGLE' DN
CR

GOB [GW 970]
MILFORD HAVEN Waterston Petroplus International
Loop GF 284.44

Controlled by Clarbeston Road Jn SC (CR)

C

26A

Alv-y-Bally (UWC) 259.96
White House Mill (UWC) 260.54
Llwyngwydd No. 2 (UWC) 261.28
Llwyngwydd No. 2 (UWC) 261.06
Masons No. 1 (UWC) 261.17
Dayfarm (UWC) 262.66
Crinow Farm No. 2 (UWC) 263.64
Upper Chapel Hill Farm (UWC) 265.37
[ARBERTH] NARBERTH 264.08
4
Narberth Tunnel (273 yards) 264.29-16
Ornoe House Farm (UWC) 266.65

GW : Pembroke & Tenby [GW 950] PEM

Knighton Crossing (UWC) 271.14
Kilwen (UWC) 270.27
Moreton Crossing (UWC) 271.22
[CILGETI] KILGETTY 269.62
6
SAUNDERSFOOT 270.41
5
Hilling (UWC) 272.11
Cross (UWC) 279.00

Miles from Paddington via Stroud

GW [GW 960] : South Wales
JOHNSTON 280.67
5
MIL SWM 2 [GW 960]
280.70 (Johnston Jn)

Controlled by Whitland SB (W)

Tenby or Greenhill Vdct (136 yards) 274.53
[DINBYCH-Y-PYSGOD] TENBY 274.46-39
7
274.46
Penally Court 275.71
[PENALUN] PENALLY
7
275.71
Penally Mod (UWC) 276.95
2.72
[MAENORBYR] MANORBIER 279.09
5
Norchard Farm No. 1 (AOCL) 279.06
Norton Farm (UWC) 280.17
2.18
Nortland Farm No.1 2.72
Beavers Hill (open) 280.82 / 280.52
Newton Lodge (UWC) 280.63
Beavers Hill Farm (UWC) 280.35
c b a

[PENFRO] PEMBROKE 284.11
6
[LLANDYFAI] LAMPHEY 282.50
5

Pembroke Tunnel (460 yards) 285.75
Lamphey (open) 285.26 / 285.06
Pembroke Dock East GF 285.26 / 285.76
[DOC PENFRO] PEMBROKE DOCK 286.21
1
Pembroke Dock Station GF 286.14
6
Ramp 286.26

a = Bier Hill (UWC) 279.18
b = Sunny Hill Farm No. 2 (UWC) 279.34
c = Sunny Hill Farm No. 5 (UWC) 279.48

D

4 : 22A : to Shrewsbury

UP HEREFORD
DOWN HEREFORD

English Bridge Jn

SHREWSBURY

Coleham Depot
Abbey Foregate Vdct 0.00
0.39-32
4 : 22A : to Abbey Foregate Jn

Sidings: 1 & 2 ETRMS 4 & 5 OTM
Loading Docks
Servicing Shed
GW 733 SBAT
GW & LMS (LNW), Jt: Shrewsbury & Welshpool
WELSHPOOL H 0.00
Sutton Bridge Jn SB (SB) 0.65
for Welshpool route 0.68
4 : 23C : to Dovey Jn
UP GOODS LOOP 0.72
DOWN MAIN
UP MAIN 1.317

1.31

SHREWSBURY to HEREFORD LINE
SHL [GW 730] GW : LMS (LNW) Joint : Shrewsbury & Hereford

Tarmac GF (oou) 2.77
Bayston Hill Tarmac
New House Farm (UWC) 3.45
Micklewood No. 2 (UWC) 4.26 (Condover)
All Stretton No. 1 (UWC) 8.10
All Stretton No. 2 (UWC) 7.24
Dorrington (DR) 6.25
All Stretton No. 1 (UWC) 1.38
8
CHURCH STRETTON 12.63
613 ft 12.06
1
2
Ox Mill (UWC) 15.06
Marsh Farm HABD 14.33
Woodlands (UWC) 14.86
13.35
(MOB) (UWC)
Marshbrook (MB) 15.29

Miles from Shrewsbury Station
Zero = 171m 49ch (Paddington mileage)

27A : to Hereford

26 August 2010

© Copyright **TRACKmaps**. No reproduction without permission

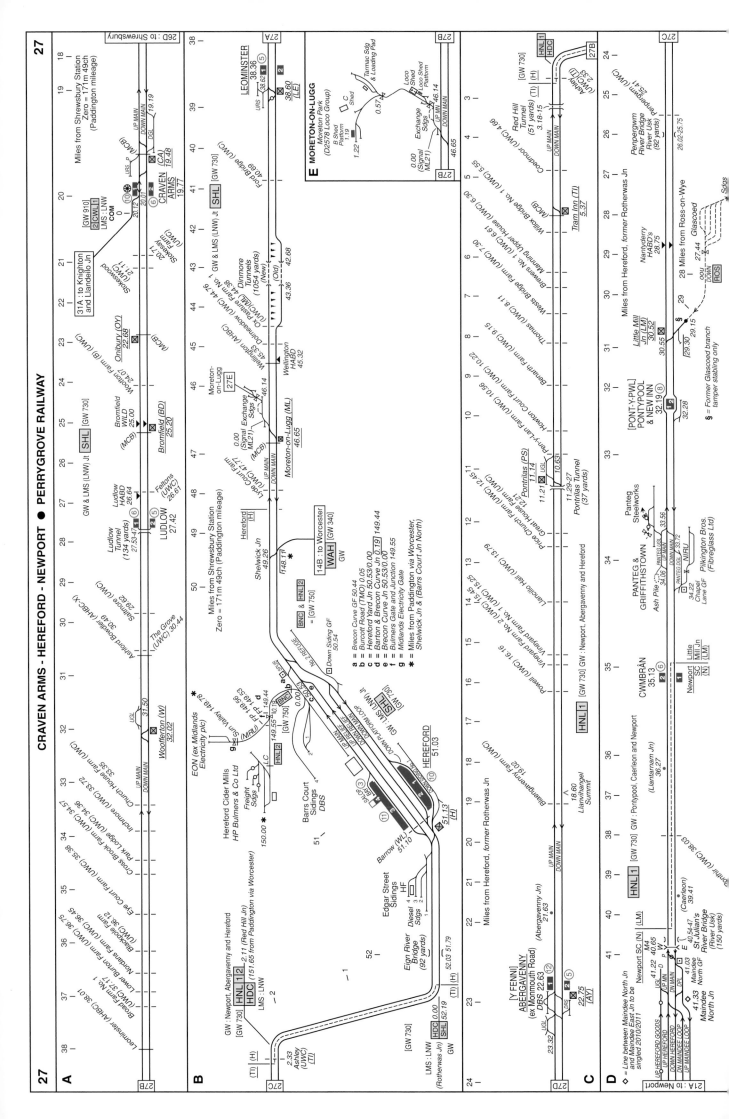

A

: to Newport   21A

GW : Monmouthshire Railway & Canal

Park Jn   Park North   1.10 1.02   160.24

WVL [GW 770]

DOWN MAIN / UP MAIN   M4   E

1.45   W 1.57   1.40 Auxiliary Token Instrument

2.05 /0.00   Bassaleg Jn (Bassaleg Jn)

Rhiwderin (AOCL) 1.35

Keepers (UWC) 2.49   Machen Fach Farm (UWC) 2.68

DOWN   Bassaleg Vdct 0.19

'MACHEN QUARRY' SINGLE

UP

BJR [GW 773]   GW : Brecon & Merthyr (Rumney Railway)

Machen Quarry Outlet GF 3.50

Risca Sth Jn 4.11   ROGERSTONE [Y TY-DY] 3.01

RISCA & PONTYMISTER [RHISCA A PHONT-Y MEISTER] 5.12

THROUGH QUARRY LINE 4.19 / CR 4.06 / WB 4.19   4.19

MACHEN QUARRY: Hanson Quarry Products

Machen Quarry Inlet GF 4.45   4.69

Line Kiln 6.15   CCTV 6.15

CROSSKEYS 7.06 (5)   Crosskeys Jn 7.15

Halls Viaduct 7.67

Miles from Newport, Ebbw Junction

Lines controlled by Newport, Park Junction SB (PJ)

[TRECELYN] NEWBRIDGE 10.45

(Crumlin LL) 11.39   11.48 (Crumlin Viaduct over)

9.24 (Abercarn)

LLANHILLETH (5) 13.29   14.23 (Aberbeeg Jn)

[GW 770]   EBW WVL

'EBBW VALE SINGLE'   UP EBBW VALE SINGLE

15.64 (Graig Fawr SB)

Cwm (FP) 16.55

EBBW VALE PARKWAY [PARCFFORD GLYN EBWY] 18.35

18.42

GW : Monmouthshire Railway & Canal

B

Miles from Cardiff (Bute East Dock)

Caerphilly Tunnel (1 mile, 181 yards)   E 5.58 M4   6.06

LISVANE & THORNHILL [LLYSFAEN A DRAENEN PEN-Y-GRAIG]   W 5.45

LLANISHEN 4.61

HEATH HIGH LEVEL [LEFEL UCHEL Y MYNYDD BYCHAN] 3.52

Heath Vdct   Heath Jn 3.32 / 3.29 (HJ)   SB (HJ)

3.62 / 3.59   0.15

HEATH LOW LEVEL [LEFEL ISELY MYNYDD BYCHAN] 0.29

Cardiff SC (C)

CAR [GW 810]   GW : Rhymney   'VALLEY LINES'

UP CAERPHILLY / DOWN CAERPHILLY

COM   1.22   1.17 Queen Street North Jn

CARDIFF QUEEN STREET [CAERDYDD HEOL Y FRENHINES] 1.08

CAM [GW 830] GW : TV

Queen Street South Jn 0.66

[1] [2] [3]   1.04

22 : to Cardiff   CEJ   /0.22/

[CAERFFILI] CAERPHILLY 8.21 (11)

'Rhymney Valley'

ABER 8.70

[LLWYNBEDW] BIRCHGROVE 1.37

TY GLAS 1.20

RHIWBINA 1.78

Miles from former Heath Jn 0.00/3.17 CAR

CAR [GW 810] GW : Rhymney

Umbrella 1.55-51

CATHAYS 1.61

Miles from Cardiff Docks (Bute Road/BAY)

LLANBRADACH Dn 10.60/ Up 10.74

DOWN MAIN / UP MAIN

CAR [GW 810] GW : Rhymney

[YR EGLWYS NEWYDD] WHITCHURCH 2.25

Miles from Cardiff (Bute East Dock)

Ystrad Mynach South Jn 13.41   URS

Ystrad Mynach (YM) 13.33

CRY [GW 828] GW : Cardiff

CORYTON 2.57   2.58 (3)

GW : Rhymney   12.72

Heath Jn SB (HJ)   13.62   PTA VON   GW

TREDOMEN   15.01 Dn 13.57 / 12.41 Up 13.63

YSTRAD MYNACH (Dn 13.57 Up 13.63) (6)

HENGOED 14.55

DN MAIN / UP MAIN

3 Miles from Cardiff Docks (Bute Road/BAY)

GW : Taff Vale   CAM [GW 830]

'CITY LINES'

PENGAM 16.30

(BD) (YM)   Gibbons (UWC) 15.40

Llancaiach Isaf (UWC) 13.26   13.36

(Trelewis) 14.43

GW : Taff Bargoed Joint   TBD VON GW

(Taff Bargoed Branch Jn)

Bargoed South 17.54   BARGOED 18.03

(BD) 18.07 / 18.09   DN DUMP SDG 18.21-15 / 18.26/18.09

Bargoed Viaduct (120 yards)

GILFACH FARGOED 17.35

Miles from Pontypool Road via Crumlin HL

(Bedlinog) 17.02

CWMBARGOED Argent   'CWMBARGOED'

LLANDAF [GW 840] 4.27 (VR) (C)

Radyr Jn 4.64   Taff Vdct (48 yds)

3.60/0.00 (Roath Branch Jn)

DN MAIN / UP MAIN

GW : Rhymney   CAR [GW 810]

BRITHDIR 19.31

TIR-PHIL 20.40

CWMBARGOED 19.59   NR Bdy

Cwmbargoed Crossing (TMO) 20.37

RADYR 5.32   Radyr North Jn 5.40

Radyr Jn SC (VR) 5.28 / 5.23   Radyr Jn SC (VR)

Cardiff Jn SC (C)   Cardiff West

Pentyrch: Afon Taff Vdct (66 yards) 6.51

Gelynis (FP X) 6.20   7.10

TAFF'S WELL [FFYNNON TAFF] 7.24

Taff's Well: Afon Taff Vdct (88 yards) 7.74

GW : Taff Vale   CAM [GW 830]

RAD GW : Taff Vale

DANESCOURT 3.18

Radyr Jn SC (VR)

23A : to Cardiff via Ninian Park

(VR = Valleys-Radyr)

Miles from Cardiff via Ninian Park

PONTLOTTYN [PONTLOTTYN] 22.65

Pontlottyn Viaduct (128 yards) 23.00/22.75

Impress Metal Packaging 23.31

Read's GF   Rhymney Sidings South GF 23.51

Gelligaer and Hafod Quarries 20.75

CWMBARGOED [Tai Cwm Bargoed] 20.66 / 20.41

Colliery Crossing 20.70

29A : to Pontypridd

[RHYMNI] RHYMNEY 23.64 (6)   24.00

'RHYMNEY'

© Copyright TRACKmaps. No reproduction without permission

August 2010

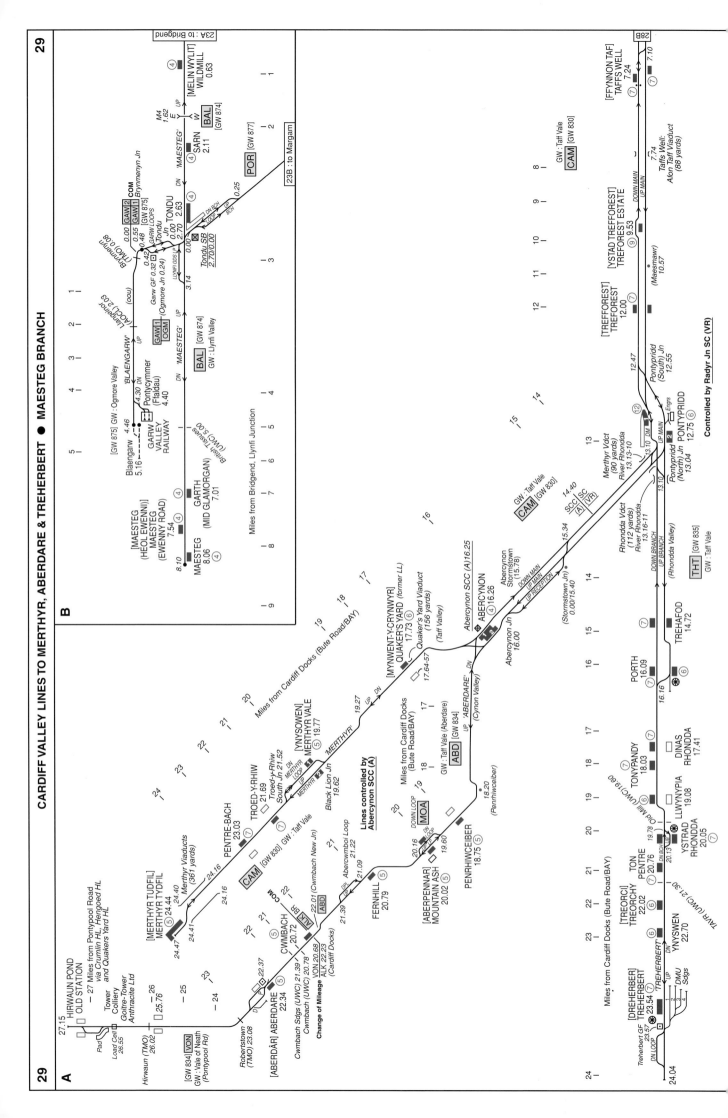

A

[Y BARRI] BARRY 8.12
Barry Jn 0.00
0.52 UP MN 0.45 DN MN
0.77
Porthkerry Tunnel No.1 (543 yards)
Porthkerry Viaduct (376 yards) 1.67-1.50
1.73
Porthkerry Tunnel No.2 (73 yards) 1.76
8.16
Barry Island

(CCTV)
RHOOSE* 3.22
* Rhoose for Cardiff International Airport [Maes Awyr Rhyngwladol Caerdydd y Rhws]

VOG [GW 870] GW : Barry

4.64
Coal Sdgs
Cement Sdg
Lafarge
[Aberddawan] Aberthaw SB 5.03
Engrs DPL
EWS
Reception Sdgs 5.19
Aberthaw Cement GF 5.36
5.27
5.69
5.76 Loop Jn
7.60
Flyash Sdg

ABERTHAW POWER STATION LINE
APS (Private Line)

6.47
ABERTHAW POWER STATIONS
INNOGY Power
'B' Power Station WB
Hopper Wagon Discharge WB
LC 7.13
6.73
7.17
NIRU
INNOGY Control Panel 7.06
LS
'A' Power Station
NIRU

(St Athan) 8.31
Church Farm (UWC) 7.09

LLANTWIT MAJOR [LLANILLTUD FAWR] 9.55
VOG [GW 870] GW : Barry

Landow (UWC) 13.72
Farmers (UWC) 13.25

UP VOG DOWN VOG
15.07 (Southerndown Road)

to Waterton
Fords Siding GF 18.00
Fords Junction 17.78/0.00
Controlled by Cowbridge Road (CR)

23A : to Bridgend and Waterton

22 : to Cardiff

VALLEY LINES
GW [GW 830] BRY : Barry

EASTBROOK 3.40
DINAS POWYS 4.18

Barry Docks Low Level Line Jn 5.74
Barry Docks Low Level Line Jn 6.19
Barry SB (B) Cardiff SC (C)

[TREGATWG] CADOXTON 6.10
Cadoxton Down Rec GF 6.19

BARRY DOCKS L.L. LINE
BDO
GW : Barry BRY [GW 830]

LOW LEVEL LINE No.1
ABP : NR 6.69

Scrap Yard Compound (Barry Dunn Bros Ltd)
Wimborne Road LC 7.59
Atlantic Way
LC's Wimborne Rd 8.07
VCM DISCHARGE (closed) 8.04

[DOCIAUR BARRI] BARRY DOCKS 6.78

BARRY DOCKS
ASSOCIATED BRITISH PORTS

David Davies Road LC
Coal Wharf Bulk Discharge Berth
Dock No.2
LOW LEVEL LINES DOCK No.2
Container Terminal
Grain Mill RHM
Aggregate Terminal
RHM = Rank Hovis McDougall
Shed
BARRY MOORS

former Guerets Works Line
Fresh Water Reservoir
Loco Shed
Cadoxton River
SULLY MOORS
Dow Chemicals
LC's

Note: Dock lines shown may not be always up-to-date

B

WOODHAM HALT 7.73
GW : Barry BRY [GW 830]

GLADSTONE BRIDGE 7.40
Former Hood Road Goods Shed
WATERFRONT (7.66 former Docks LL line mileage) 0.35

UP 7.69 DOWN
7.76 7.77
0.31 0.39
Heritage Skills Centre
0.28
LC's 0.24

BARRY TOURIST RAILWAY (Operator: Cambrian Transport Ltd)
Incline down to 0.00 8.36 Docks Branch Jn

Barry Island Viaduct (153 yards)
8.56
8.49
[YNYS Y BARRI] BARRY ISLAND 8.70
BRY [GW 830] GW : Barry

Barry Island Railway Heritage Centre
PLYMOUTH ROAD 9.08
Pit 9.01
Possible future lines to Barry Pier
9.76

(Barry Pier) 9.34

Barry Harbour
Dock No.1
Junction Cut
No.3 Dock Basin
Lady Windsor Lock
Entrance Channel
West Breakwater
East Breakwater
Jackson's Bay
Whitmore Bay

[Y BARRI] BARRY 8.12
Barry Jn 0.00
SB (B) 8.07
8.16
LONG SDG
UP BRANCH DOWN BRANCH
Stores
Coal Stage
Pits

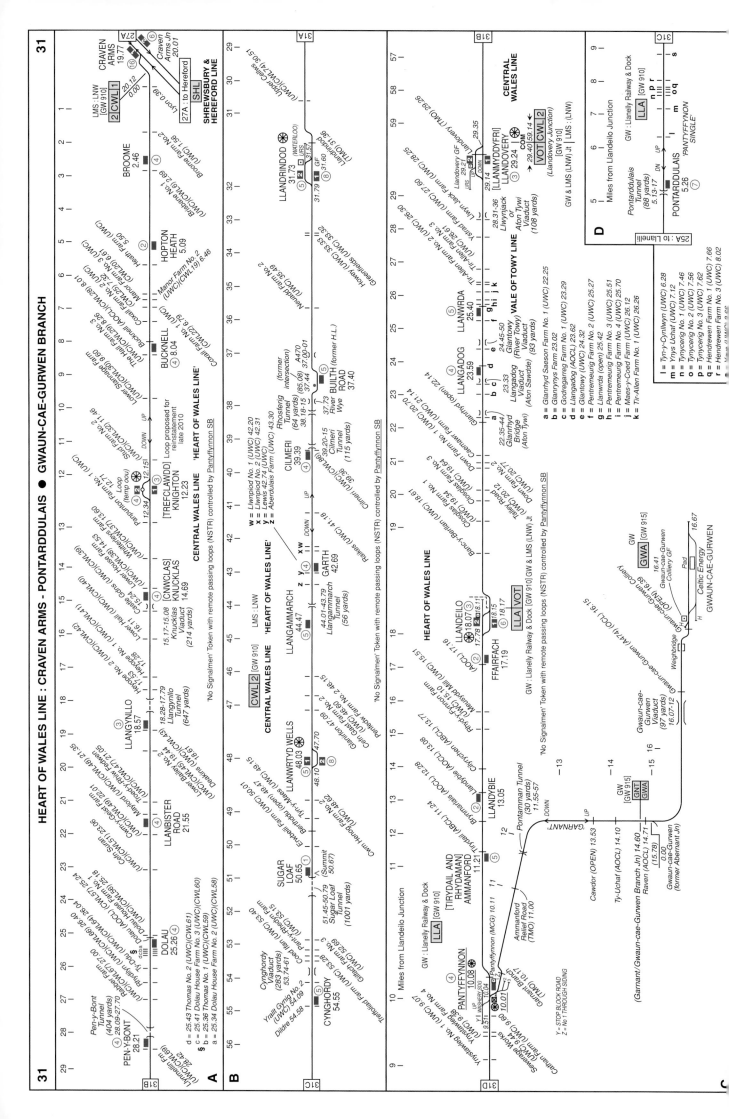

VARIOUS MINOR RAILWAYS

A GLOUCESTERSHIRE WARWICKSHIRE RAILWAY plc 1435mm / 4' 8½" gauge

Miles from Honeybourne East Loop Jn

19   18   17   16   15   14   13   12   11   10   9   8   7

End of Line
19.22

CHELTENHAM RACECOURSE

Hunting Butts Tunnel 97yds

GOTHERINGTON HALT 15.33 (request)

(Bishops Cleeve) 16.76

15.40
15.60

Gotherington West (private platform)
(Not commissioned) SB

Greet Tunnel (693 yards)

WINCHCOMBE 12.00

Freight Bay
PW SDG

Carriage & Wagon Sdgs

12.25
12.57

13.36 (Gretton)

HCL   GW

10.40 (Hales Abbey)
9.60

DOWN   UP

TODDINGTON 9.36
9.48

Loco pit
Locomotive sheds
Unloading Road

9.00

1   2   O

7.25

LAVERTON LOOP

7.02
proposed extension To Broadway 4.73

Details courtesy of P.E. Scott

B BUCKINGHAMSHIRE RAILWAY CENTRE (Quainton Railway Society Ltd) 1435mm / 4' 8½" gauge

Up Yard

REWLEY ROAD STATION

Traverser

QUAINTON ROAD
44.22
44.17

3 MJC 2

Down Yard

NETWORK RAIL

Miles from Baker Street (Met.) 44

43.70

N

Details courtesy of P.E. Scott

C AVON VALLEY RAILWAY 1435mm / 4' 8½" gauge

Meadowcourt footpath 127.65

OLDLAND COMMON 127.32   127.37½

HS   LOOP   MAIN

127.26

Bitton North GF PW 128.20
Bitton North footpath 128.18½
SIGNAL BOX SDG
128.27   SHED ROAD PW 128.33

Loco Shed & Workshop

3   2   1   MAIN   LOOP

Bitton South GF 128.26
BITTON STATION GF 128.34
Bitton Station SB 128.26
BITTON 128.36

Bitton South GF 128.36
Bitton South footpath 128.56½

128.76

128   128¼   128½   128¾   129

DOWN →

River Boyd 129.45
129.54 River Avon

AVON RIVERSIDE 129.63
129.68

Former LMS: Midland Railway: Bath Branch   MBL

Miles from London Rd Jn (Derby) via Whitacre, Camp Hill and Gloucester (Eastgate)

Miles from Whitacre, Camp Hill and Gloucester (Eastgate)

D TEIFI VALLEY RAILWAY (on BR trackbed) 60cm / 1' 11½" gauge

CAN   GW : Carmarthen & Newcastle Emlyn

PONT GOCH (Teifi River) (269.45)

LLANDYFRIOG (268.78)

Vdct (268.40-38)

PONTPRENSHITW (268.32)

FOREST HALT (268.15)

HENLLAN (267.76)

(HENLLAN) BR Station (267.68)   (267.63)   LS

Proposed extn to Pentrecwrt (265.48)

Miles from Paddington via Carmarthen & Pencader Jn (260.61)
(No mileposts remain)

Details courtesy of P.E. Scott

E SWINDON AND CRICKLADE RAILWAY 1435mm / 4' 8½" gauge

(towards Cricklade 39.13)

South Meadow Lane 0.75

HAYES KNOLL 0.41 (37.17)

Hayes Oak Sidings
Loco Shed

Tadpole Lane

(36.62)
BLUNSDON 0.02 (36.58)   (36.56)

River Ray

Swindon   36.49   c 35.29

Former Midland and South Western Junction Line

Old BR distances in brackets (from Andover Red Post Jn)

N

Details courtesy of P.E. Scott

F DIDCOT RAILWAY CENTRE (Great Western Society Ltd.)

'OXFORD ROAD'

'EYNSHAM'

DEMONSTRATION LINE
BRANCH LINE

Carriage Shed
Transfer Shed
'BURLESCOMBE'
Frome Mineral Jn SB

Traverser
Loco Works
Lifting Shop
Loco Shed

Coaling stage

former Centre Yard Sidings

7' 0¼" & 4' 8½" mixed gauge
7' 0¼" gauge

DIDCOT HALT
LC   Radstock SB

G CHOLSEY AND WALLINGFORD RAILWAY

WAL

3C

WALLINGFORD 2.26
2.29

STORAGE SDG

2.14

Wallingford By-pass (ABCL)
1.72
Winterbrook LC 1.60

Winterbrook Lane LC 1.60

1   1½   2   2¼

Miles from London Rd Jn (Derby) etc

Details courtesy of P.E. Scott

H BRISTOL INDUSTRIAL MUSEUM (Bristol Harbour Railway)
Bristol City Council

PRINCE STREET   BHB

Wapping Road

Princes Wharf (oou)

INDUSTRIAL MUSEUM

S.S. "GREAT BRITAIN"

Floating Harbour

Wapping Wharf

BRISTOL HARBOUR BRANCH

A = Quay Loop GF
B = Buttery GF
C = Butterfly Jn
D = Smeaton Road loco shed

A   B

CREATE CENTRE   BWM

WAPPING WHARF BRANCH
former Wapping Wharf SDG

0.00 / 119.27

GW : Bristol Harbour Extn
Harbour Extn 0.15

CUTTING

Harbour Extn 0.15
0.72 Ashton (Swing) Bridge (R. Avon : New Cut)
*Ashton Bridge LC (open) 0.65

New Cut
0.65   0.70

D

(The Museum is under reconstruction and is closed until 2011. The Harbour Railway continues to operate)

Details courtesy of P.E. Scott

J BRECON MOUNTAIN RAILWAY Co Ltd 1' 11¾" gauge

PANT 18.71
18.48

18.73
Loco shed & works

2

PONTSTICILL 17.18
17.22
Store
LS
pit

LC

1

17

Dol-y-Gaer

16.25
Forestry Commission

15.69   15.75   16

Miles from Brecon (mileposts gone)

18
*

K PONTYPOOL AND BLAENAVON RAILWAY 1435mm / 4' 8½" gauge

BLAENAVON (HIGH LEVEL) 4.59
4.65 Varteg Road
4.62
4.30 Forgeside Road

Pit Road
3.60
3.53
3.38   3.36
3.33   'Big Pit Museum'

FURNACE SIDINGS 3.36
LC
3.30
Running shed
LS

WHISTLE INN 2.77
Height 1290 ft
2.75

3   4

former LMS: LNW   'Big Pit Museum'

DN   UP

Miles from Brynmawr (LNW)

Height 1231 ft

Details courtesy of P.E. Scott

L RHEILFFORDD GWILI RAILWAY / LLWYFAN CERRIG RAILWAY 1435mm / 4' 8½" gauge

Pontyfenni
248.72

BRONWYDD ARMS 249.11
249.08
249.19 footpath

CAN
Carmarthen & Newcastle Emlyn

DN   UP

250
249

DANYCOED 251.30
251

LLWYFAN CERRIG 250.57
250.50   250.23 footpath
Bridge 9 (Afon Gwili)

LS
CS

Bridge 10
to Conwil (252.14)
Afon Gwili

Trackbed to Carmarthen

Miles from Paddington via Stroud

Miles from Stroud

Details courtesy of P.E. Scott

August 2010

B CAERWENT, Defence Rail and Container Services (12 miles of track)

N

Site of Power Station

Paper Store Sdg

WEST GATE

Cordite Loading Shed

LS

MAIN GATE

Entrance Road

D (oou)

Site of Power Station

LC

J.T. Landscapes

Asbestos Stripping

EAST GATE

Former Sulphur Store

Scrapping Area

LC

Trap

NORTH BRANCH

SOUTH BRANCH

Exchange Sidings

(2½m from Caerwent Branch Jn)

1.63 from Caerwent Branch Jn

20B

Skeletal Diagram only

A DEFENCE LOGISTICS ORGANISATION : BICESTER

PIDDINGTON

'A' SITE

B4011 LC

'G' SITE

Gates

Gate

Gate

Gate

ARNCOTT

Norris Road LC

Gate G.

G.

G.

Arncott Sidings

Gate Gate LC Murcott Road

MT Sidings

AMBROSDEN

Gate Hut

'B' Cabin

Murton Roads LC

Skeletal Diagram only

Container Terminal

'D' SITE

GRAVEN HILL

PW Storage Area

Gate

QUEENS HALT

'E' SITE

C&W Railcar Shed

Loco Shed

PLATFORM

'A' Cabin

Sorting Sidings

To Bletchley

London Road Exchange Siding

Central Ordnance Depot GF 19.50

13A

To Oxford

Index

Index of Locations

This index covers practically all the named locations on the maps to assist the reader in their search. Stations are listed in capitals, signal boxes with their codes and level crossings with their type. FP and Barrow crossings in the maps are not carried to the index nor are trunk and motorway overbridges. Locations of now-defunct assets are given in brackets and private and preserved railway locations appear in italics, followed by an abbreviation in brackets indicating the parent line.

Location	Ref
Hyde Park Siding (Exeter)	7A
Ifton Hill Farm LC (UWC)	20B
Inchmore LC (UWC)	27A
Inkpens No.1 LC (UWC)	13B
Iron Acton By-Pass LC (TMO)	16B
Iron Acton Station LC (AOCL)	16B
Iscoed LC (UWC)	26A
ISLIP	13A
Islip LC (R/G)	13A
IVER	2B
Ivy Lane LC (UWC)	13D
IVYBRIDGE	7C
Ivybridge Viaduct	7C
Jeffries LC (UWC)	13C
Jersey Marine Jn North	24A
Jersey Marine Jn South	24A
JOHNSTON	26B
Keen's LC (UWC)	20A
Keepers LC (UWC)	28A
Keinton Mandevill HABD	12B
KEMBLE	15A
Kemble GF	15A
Kemble Tunnel	15A
Kennaway Tunnel	7B
Kennel & Avon Canal East Viaduct	11B
Kennel & Avon Canal West Viaduct	11B
Kennet Bridge (Reading)	3A, 3D
Kennet Bridge Loop	3A
Kennington Jn	12C
Kennington Jn LC (UWC)	12C
Kennington Viaduct	12C
Kensal Green Servicing Platform	1A
Kernick North GF	9C
Kernick Siding (Imerys)	9C
Kernick South GF	9C
KEYHAM	8B
Keyham East & West GFs	8B
Keyham HABD	8B
Keyham Viaduct	8B
KEYNSHAM	5A
(Kidlington)	13B
KIDWELLY	25B
Kidwelly Branch Jn	25B
Kidwelly Jn	25B
Kidwelly LC (MCB)	25B
Kidwelly SB (K)	25B
Kidwelly Viaduct	25B
Kilawen Farm LC (UWC)	26C
KILBURN (LU)	18C
Kilburn Viaduct	18C
KILGETTY	26C
Kingford Viaduct	10C
KINGHAM	13B
KINGS NYMPTON	10C
KINGS SUTTON	13B
(Kingskerswell)	7C
Kingsland Road Sidings GF	5B
Kingswear Bay GF (DSR)	7C
KINGSWEAR for DARTMOUTH (DSR)	7C
Kingswear South GF (DSR)	7C
KINTBURY	11B
Kintbury HABD	11B
Kintbury LC (MCB)	11B
Knapton's LC (UWC)	13B
KNIGHTON	31A
Knightson Farm LC (UWC)	26C
KNUCKLAS	31A
Knucklas Viaduct	31A
Ladbroke Grove	1A
(Lady Down Aqueduct)	11C
Lafarge Aggregates LC (TMO)	2B
Lafarge No.1 GF	2B
Lafarge No.2 GF	2B
Laira Jn	8A
Laira Viaduct	8A
LAMPHEY	26C
Landeilo Jn Sidings (DBS)	25A
Landore Jn	24A
Landore TMD (FGW)	24A
Landore Viaduct	24A
Landsand LC (UWC) (DR)	10C
Langford Lane LC (AOCL)	13A
LANGLEY	2B
Langley East	2B
Langport (Foal Mead) Viaduct	12B
(Langport East)	12B
Lanjeth LC (Open)	9B
(Lansdown Jn)	15D
Lansdown Loop (Cheltenham)	15D
LAPFORD	10C
Lapford North GF	10C
Lapford South GF	10C
Lashbrooke Viaduct	3A
Latteridge LC (TMO)	16B
LAUNTON	13A
Launton LC (AOCL)	13A
Lavington Viaduct	11C
(Lavington)	11C
LAWRENCE HILL	16B
Lawrence Hill GF	16B
(Laycock)	4C
Leckwith Loop North Jn	22
Leckwith Loop South Jn	22
Leckwith Road Bridge GF	22
LEDBURY	14B
Ledbury SB (L)	14B
Ledbury Tunnel	14B
Ledbury Viaduct	14B
Lee Moor China Clay Crossing (PVR)	8D
Leigh Wood LC (AOCL) (WSR)	6D
LELANT	10B
LELANT SALTINGS	10B
Lenthay LC (UWC)	17B
LEOMINSTER	27A, 27B
Leominster LC	27A
Leominster SB (LE)	27B
Leonard's Mill Viaduct	12A
Letterston East GF	26B
Letterston Jn	26B
Letterston West GF	26B
Lewis LC (UWC)	31B
Lewis No.1 LC (UWC)	14A
Lewis No.2 LC (UWC)	14A
Ley LC (MG)	20A
Lickey Incline	15B
Lime Kiln LC (CCTV)	28A
(Limpley Stoke)	4C
Lipson Jn	8A
(Lipson Vale)	8B
Liskeard GF	9A
Liskeard Jn SB (LD)	9A
Liskeard Viaduct	9A
Little Bourton LC (UWC)	13C
Little Harmiston LC UWC	26B
LITTLE KIMBLE	19B
Little Mill Jn SB (LM)	27D
(Little Somerford)	14C
Little Treviscoe FP LC (Open)	9C
Little Weir Farm No.2 LC	10C
Littleton & Badsey LC (CCTV)	13D
LLANBISTER ROAD	31A
Llanboidy LC (AHBC)	26A
LLANBRADACH	28B
Llancaiach Isaf LC (UWC)	28B
Llancillo Hall LC (UWC)	27C
LLANDAF	28B
Llandaff Viaduct (Afon Taff)	28B
Llandarcy GF	24A
LLANDEILO	31C
Llandeilo Jn	25A
Llandeilo Jn East Sidings GF	25A
Llandeilo Jn West Sidings GF	25A
LLANDOVERY	31C
Llandovery GF	31C
Llandovery Jn	31C
Llandovery LC (TMO)	31C
Llandow LC (UWC)	30A
LLANDRINDOD	31B
Llandrindod GF	31B
Llandrindod LC (TMO)	31B
LLANDYBIE	31C
Llandybie LC (AOCL)	31C
LLANDYFRIOG (TVR)	32D
LLANELLI	25A
Llanelli Dock Jn East GF	25A
Llanelli East LC (CCTV)	25A
Llanelli West LC (MCB)	25A
LLANGADOG	31C
Llangadog LC (AOCL)	31C
Llangadog Viaduct	31C
LLANGAMMARCH	31B
Llangammarch Tunnel	31B
Llangeinor LC (AOCL)	29B
LLANGENNECH	25A
Llangennech LC (UWC)	25A
Llangyfelach Summit	25A
Llangyfelach Tunnel	25A
LLANGYNLLO	31A
Llangynllo Tunnel	31A
LLANHARAN	23A
Llanharan LC (UWC)	23A
(Llanharan)	23A
LLANHILLETH	28A
LLANISHEN	28B
Llanlliwe Farm LC (UWC)	26A
Llanlon LC (Open)	26C
LLANSAMLET	24A
Llanstephan FP LC (R/G)	25B
(Llantarnam Jn)	27D
Llantrisant	23A
Llantrisant West LC (MCB) (CCTV)	23A
LLANTWIT MAJOR	30A
Llanvihangel Summit (UWC)	27C
Llanwern Steel Works	20C
Llanwern West Jn	20C
Llanwern Works East Connection	20C
Llanwern Works West Connection	20C
LLANWRDA	31C
Llanwrda LC (Open)	31
LLANWRTYD	31
Lliswerry Sidings	21
LISKEARD	9
LISVANE & THORNHILL	28
Llwnpiod No.1 LC (UWC)	31
Llwnpiod No.2 LC (UWC)	31
Llwyn Jack Farm LC (UWC)	31
Llwyndrysi LC (UWC)	26
Llwyndyrys LC (UWC)	26
LLWYNFAN CERRIG (RGR)	32
Llwyngwyddil No.2 LC (UWC)	26
Llwynllanc Farm No.1 LC (UWC)	24
LLWYNYPIA	29
Llwypener No.2 LC (UWC)	26
Llynfi Goods Loop	29
Llynfi Jn	23
Llynmellin Farm LC (UWC)	31
Llywnjack Viaduct	31
(Lockinge)	4
Loco Yard (Swindon)	15
Lodge Farm LC (Open)	9
LONDON MARYLEBONE	18
LONDON PADDINGTON	1
London Road Exchange Siding (Bicester)	13A, 33
London Yard (Worcester)	14
(Londover)	26
(Long Ashton)	6
Long Dyke Jn	21B, 2
Long Dyke Jn GF	21B, 2
Long Marston (Motor Rail Logistics)	13
Long Marston GF	13
Long Rock Depot (FGW)	10
Long Rock LC (CCTV)	10
(Longfield)	2
(Lonlas Jn)	24
Lonlas Tunnel	24
LOOE	9
Lookout LC (UWC)	25
LOSTWITHIEL	9
Lostwithiel Fowey Branch Jn	9
Lostwithiel Milk Siding GF	9
Lostwithiel SB (LL)	9
Lostwithiel Station LC (MCB)	9
Lostwithiel Viaduct (R. Fowey)	9
Lougher Viaduct	25
Lower Bailey No.2 LC (UWC)	31
Lower Barn Farm LC (UWC)	20
Lower Burton Farm LC (UWC)	27
Lower Hall LC (UWC)	31
Lower House Farm LC (UWC)	31
Lower Stannage Farm LC (UWC)	31
LUDLOW	27
Ludlow HABD	27
Ludlow Tunnel	27
LUXULYAN	9
Luxulyan Tunnel	9
Lyde Court Farm LC (UWC)	27
LYDNEY	20
Lydney A48 LC (TMO) (DFR)	20
Lydney Bypass LC (ABCL) (DFR)	20B, 20
Lydney GF	20
Lydney Jn SB (DFR)	20
LYDNEY JUNCTION (DFR)	20
Lydney LC (MCB)	20
LYDNEY TOWN (DFR)	20
LYMPSTONE COMMANDO	18
LYMPSTONE VILLAGE	18
Lyneham LC (UWC)	13
Lyon LC	31
(M&SW Jn Underbridge)	15
Machen Fach Farm LC (UWC)	28
Machen Quarry	28
Machen Quarry Inlet GF	28
Machen Quarry Outlet GF	28
(Maesglas Intersection)	21
Maesglas Tip	21
Maesmawr LC (Open)	25
(Maesmawr)	29
MAESTEG	29
MAESTEG EWENNY ROAD	29
Maes-y-Coed Farm LC (UWC)	31
Magor Crossovers	20
MAIDEN NEWTON	18
MAIDENHEAD	2
Maidenhead East	2
Maidenhead HABD	2
Maidenhead Viaduct (R. Thames)	2
Main Down Viaduct (Bristol)	5
Main River Viaduct (Bristol)	5
Maindee East Jn	21
Maindee Engineers Depot	21
Maindee Engineers Sdg GF	21
Maindee North GF	27
Maindee North Jn	21
Maindee West Jn	21
Maindy Bach LC (UWC)	23
(Malago Vale)	5
Maliphant Crossing LC (TMO)	24
Maliphant Sidings	24

Location	Ref
MALVERN LINK	14B
Malvern Wells Signal Box	14B
Manning Upper House LC (UWC)	27C
Manor Farm LC (UWC) (Radley)	12C
Manor Farm LC (UWC) (Banbury)	13B
Manor Farm LC (UWC) (Melksham)	4C
Manor Farm No.2 LC (UWC)	31A
Manor Farm No.3 LC (UWC)	31A
MANORBIER	26C
Manorbier Newton LC (Open)	26C
Manorbier Station LC (AOCL)	26C
Mantles Wood	18E
Manuels Farm No.2 LC (UWC)	9C
(Marazion)	10B
Mare Brook LC (UWC)	13D
Mare's LC (UWC)	14A
Margam Abbey Steel Works	23D
(Margam Abbey West)	23C
Margam Abbey Works East Jn	23B
Margam East	23C
Margam Flyover	23B
Margam Knuckle Yard (DBS)	23B
Margam Middle Jn	23C
Margam Moor Jn	23B
Margam Yard (DBS)	23B
Margam Yard Jn	23C
(Margam Halt)	23C
(Margam West)	23C
Marina LC (Bourne End) (ABCL)	3B
Marina LC (CCTV) (DSR)	7C
Marley Tunnels (A38T)	7C
MARLOW	3B
Marlow Viaduct	3B
Marsh Barton	7B
Marsh Farm HABD	26D
Marsh Junction Depot	5B
Marsh Lane LC (ABCL)	19B
Marsh Mill North Jn (PVR)	8D
MARSH MILLS (PVR)	8D
Marsh Mills China Clay Works	8A
Marsh Mills No.1 LC (TOC)	8A
Marsh Mills No.2 LC (TOC)	8A
Marsh Up GF	5B
Marshbrook LC (MCB)	26D
Marshbrook SB (MB)	26D
Marshfield	21B
Marshfield HABD	21B
Marshfield WILD	21B
Marshwood Farm No.2 LC (UWC)	17B
(Marston Crossing)	4A
(Marston Magna)	17B
Marylebone IECC (ME)	18C
Masons No.1 LC (UWC)	26C
Master's LC (UWC)	12A
Maylord LC (UWC)	31A
Meadowcourt FP LC (AVR)	32C
Meads Farm LC (UWC)	18A
Meads LC (R/G-X)	6B
Meldon East GF	10C
Meldon Quarry (Bardon Aggregates)	10C
MELDON QUARRY (DR)	10C
Meldon Station GF (DR)	10C
Meldon Viaduct	10C
MELKSHAM	4C
(Mells Road)	12A
Menadue LC (UWC)	9B
Mendip Rail (Hanson) Sidings (Islip)	13A
MENDIP VALE (ESR)	12A
MENHENIOT	9A
Merebank Sidings	17A
Merehead (Mendip Rail Ltd)	12A
Merehead Halt	12A
Merehead Quarry Jn	12A
Merehead Stone Terminal (Foster Yeoman)	12A
Merehead West	12A
MERRYFIELD LANE (ESR)	12A
Merthyr Jn GF	29A
MERTHYR TYDFIL	29A
MERTHYR VALE	29A
Merthyr Viaduct	29A
Meusydd Mill LC (UWC)	31C
Micklewood No.2 LC (UWC)	26D
Middle Forge Jn (DFR)	20D
Middle Hill Tunnel	4C
Middle Sdg East GF (Bristol T.M.)	5B
Middleway LC (CCTV)	9B
MIDGHAM	11A
Midgham LC (CCTV)	11A
(Midland Railway Overbridge)	16B
Midlands Electricity Gate (Hereford)	27B
MIDSOMER NORTON SOUTH (S&DR)	12D
MILFORD HAVEN	26B
Milford Haven Loop GF	26B
Milford Haven South GF	26B
Mill Farm Crossing LC (UWC)	18A
Millstream Jn	12C
Millstream Viaduct No.1	13A
Millstream Viaduct No.2	13A
Milltown Viaduct	9B
Milton Freight Terminal, Didcot	4A
Milton Siding	4A
(Milton)	4A
MINEHEAD (WSR)	6C
Minehead SB (WSR)	6C
Minety LC (MCG)	15A
Miskin Loops	23A
Moat Farm No.1 LC (UWC)	19B
MOD (DLO Bicester)	13A
Molinnis LC (AOCL)	9B
MONKS RISBOROUGH	19B
Monsanto GF	21A
MONTPELIER	16B
Montpelier Tunnel	16B
MOOR PARK LU)	18D
Moorswater	9A
Moorswater Crossing LC (Open)	9A
Moorswater Viaduct	9A
MORCHARD ROAD	10C
Moreton Crossing LC (UWC)	26C
Moreton Cutting	3C
Moreton Park (D2578 Loco Group)	27E
MORETON-IN-MARSH	13D
Moreton-in-Marsh SB (MM)	13D
Moreton-on-Lugg	27B
Moreton-on-Lugg LC (MCB)	27B
Moreton-on-Lugg SB (ML)	27B
Morfa Main Crossing LC	25B
Morlais Jn	25A
Morlanga LC (UWC)	23A
Morris Cowley GF	12C
Morris Hill LC (CCTV)	15D
Morriston Viaduct	25A
Moulsford Viaduct	3C
Mount Gould Jn	8A
MOUNTAIN ASH	29A
Mud Lane LC (UWC)	6A
Muddle LC	25B
Murdercombe Tunnel	12A
Mutley Tunnel	8B
Mwyndy Jn	23A
Naas LC (MCB)	20B
Nahtyoi No.2 LC (UWC)	26A
NAILSEA & BACKWELL	6A
Nailsea HABD	6A
Nanpean Wharf (Drinnick Mill)	9B
Nant-y-Cafn Farm LC (UWC)	24B
Nantyderry HABDs	27D
NAPPERS HALT (SDR)	7C
Nappers LC (Open) (SDR)	7C
NARBERTH	26C
Narberth Tunnel	26C
Narroways Hill Jn	16B
(Nass/Brookthorpe Crossing)	16A
NEASDEN (LU)	18C
Neasden Depot (LU)	18C
Neasden Jn SB (NJ)	18C
Neasden South Jn	18C
Neasden South Sidings	18C
Neasden Station Jn	18C
NEATH	24A
Neath & Brecon Jn	24B
Neath & Brecon Jn SB	24A, 24B
Neath Abbey Viaduct	24A
Neath River Swing Bridge Viaduct	24A
Neuadd Farm No.2 LC (UWC)	31B
New Cut Viaduct	24A
New House Farm LC (UWC)	26D
New Yard Depot (Exeter)	7A
NEWBRIDGE	28A
NEWBURY	11A
NEWBURY RACECOURSE	11A
Newcombes LC (UWC) (DR)	10C
Newland East LC (MCB)	14B
Newland East SB (NE)	14B
(Newlands Jn)	23B
Newnham Barton Farm LC (UWC)	10C
Newnham Tunnel	20A
NEWPORT (SOUTH WALES)	21A
Newport Docks (ABP)	21C
Newport New Tunnel	21A
Newport Old Tunnel	21A
Newport SC (N)	21A
NEWQUAY	9C
NEWTON ABBOT	7C
Newton Abbot East Crossovers	7C
Newton Abbot East Jn	7C
Newton Abbot West Jn	7C
Newton Lodge LC (UWC)	26C
NEWTON ST. CYRES	10C
Newton St. Cyres HABD	10C
Newtown West	22
NINIAN PARK	22
NORCHARD (DFR)	20D
Norchard Farm No.1 LC (UWC)	26C
Norchard SB (DFR)	20D
Nordans Farm LC (UWC)	27A
North Action Jn (LU)	19A
NORTH ACTON (LU)	1B
North Acton Jn (LU)	1B
North Devon Link Road Overbridge	6D
NORTH FILTON PLATFORM	17A
NORTH HARROW (LU)	18D
North Pole International Depot	1A
North Pole Jn	1A
North Row Viaduct	12A
North Sidings GF (Worcester)	14A
North Somerset Jn	5A, 5B
(North Somerset Railway)	12A
North Tawton (DR)	10C
North Tawton Viaduct (DR)	10C
Northcote No.2 LC	17C
NORTHOLT (LU)	19A
Northolt Jn	19A
NORTHOLT PARK	19A
Northway LC (AHBC)	15C
NORTHWICK PARK (LU)	18D
NORTHWOOD (LU)	18D
NORTHWOOD HILLS (LU)	18D
NORTON FITZWARREN (WSR)	6D
Norton Fitzwarren Jn	6D
(Norton Fitzwarren)	6D
Norton Jn	15B
Norton Jn SB (NJ)	14A, 15B
Norton No.1 LC (UWC)	10C
Norton No.2 LC (UWC)	10C
Nottar Viaduct	9A
Nuneham Viaduct	12C
Nynehead HABD	6D
Oakhampton GF (DR)	10C
Ocean Way Overbridge	22
Oddingley LC (MG)	15B
Oddington LC (AOCL)	13A
Ogmore House Farm LC (UWC)	26C
(Ogmore Jn)	29B
OKEHAMPTON	10C
Okeltor LC (Open)	8C
Old Mill LC (UWC)	26D
Old Mill LC (UWC)	29A
Old Oak Common Depots	1B
Old Oak Common East Jn	1B
Old Oak Common Flyover	1A, 1B
Old Oak Common West Jn	1B
(Old Oak Lane)	1B
(Old SB, Onllwyn)	24B
OLDFIELD PARK	4C
OLDLAND COMMON (AVR)	32C
Olds End LC (CCTV)	16A
Onibury LC (MCB)	27A
Onibury SB (OY)	27A
Onllwyn GF	24B
Onllwyn Washery	24B
Orb Works GF	21A
Over Jn	20A
Ox Pasture Farm No.1 (UWC)	27B
OXFORD	12C
Oxford Carriage Sidings	12C
Oxford North Jn	12C
OXFORD ROAD (DRC)	32F
Oxford Road Jn	3A
Oxford SB (OX)	12C
Oxford Station (Botley Rd) LC	12C
PADDINGTON (LU)	1A
Padworth Sidings	11A
PAIGNTON	7C
Paignton Crossover GF (DSR)	7C
Paignton North LC (CCTV)	7C
PAIGNTON QUEENS PARK (DSR)	7C
Paignton SB (PN)	7C
Paignton South GF	7C
Paignton South LC (TMO)	7C
Pangam LC (UWC)	21B
PANGBOURNE	3C
Panpunton Farm No.1 LC (UWC)	31A
PANT (BMR)	32J
PANTEG & GRIFFITHSTOWN	27D
PANTYFFYNNON	31C
Pantyffynnon LC (MCG)	31C
Pantyffynnon SB	31C
Pant-y-Rhedyn Farm (UWC)	31B
PAR	9B
Par Bridge LC	9B
Par Harbour (Imerys)	9B
Par Loop Jn	9B
Par SB (PR)	9B
Par Viaduct	9B
Paradise LC (UWC)	10A
Parc-y-Llong LC (Open)	9B
Park Jn	21A, 28A
Park Jn SB (PJ)	21A
Park Lodge LC (UWC)	27A
Park Royal Sidings	19A
Park Royal Stone Terminal (Tarmac)	19A
(Park Royal)	19A
Parkandillack	9C
PARKEND (DFR)	20D
PARSON STREET	5B
Parson Street Jn	5B
Parsonage Farm LC (UWC)	12C
Parsons Tunnel	7B
PATCHWAY	16B

Location	Ref
Patchway Chord	16B
Patchway Jn No.1	16B
Patchway Jn No.2	16B
Patchway New Tunnel	16B
Patchway Old Tunnel	16B
Patchway Short Tunnel	16B
(Patney & Westbury Jn)	11C
Pawlett Meads LC (UWC)	6B
PEMBREY & BURRY PORT	25A
Pembrey HABD	25A
Pembrey LC (MCB)	25A
Pembrey SB (PY)	25A
PEMBROKE	26C
PEMBROKE DOCK	26C
Pembroke Dock East GF	26C
Pembroke Dock Station GF	26C
Pembroke Tunnel	26C
Pen Mill Jn	17B
Penadlake Viaduct	9A
Penalltau Jn	28B
PENALLY	26C
Penally Court LC (UWC)	26C
Penally MOD LC (UWC)	26C
Penalt LC (UWC)	25B
PENARTH	22
Penarth Curve East No.1 GF	22
Penarth Curve East No.2 GF	22
Penarth Curve North Jn	22
Penarth Curve North No.1 GF	22
Penarth Curve South Jn	22
(Penarth Harbour Jn)	22
Penclacwydd LC (UWC)	25A
PENCOED	23A
Pencoed LC (MCB) (CCTV)	23A
Pencoed Loop	23A
Pencoed Uchaf No.1 LC (UCF)	25A
Penfedw Farm No.2 LC	31B
PENGAM	28B
Pengam Jn	21B
Penllergaer Tunnel	25A
PENMERE	10A
Penpergwm LC (UWC)	27D
Penpergwm River Bridge	27D
Penponds Viaduct	10A
PENRHIWCEIBER	29A
(Penrhiwceiber)	29A
Penrhiwlyn LC (UWC)	24A
PENRYN	10A
(Penryn Deviation)	10A
PENTRE-BACH	29A
Pentremeurig Farm No.2 LC (UWC)	31C
Pentremeurig Farm No.3 LC (UWC)	31C
Pentremeurig Farm No.4 LC (UWC)	31C
Pentyrch Viaduct (Afon Taff)	28B
Penwithers Jn	10A
Penwithers Viaduct	10A
Penybedd LC (AHBC)	25B
PEN-Y-BONT	31A
Pen-y-Bont Tunnel	31A
Pen-y-Lan Farm LC (UWC)	27C
PENZANCE	10B
Penzance HST Depot (FGW)	10B
Penzance SB (PZ)	10B
PERIVALE (LU)	19A
Perran (New) Viaduct	10A
Perran Tunnel	10A
PERRANWELL	10A
PERSHORE	14A
PEWSEY	11B
Pewsey HABD	11B
Phillot Tunnel	7B
Pibwrllwyd Crossing LC (UWC)	25B
Pier 7 Escape Shaft (Heathrow)	2D
PILL	5B
Pill Farm Crossing LC (UWC)	9B
Pill Tunnel	5B
Pill Viaduct	5B
PILNING	16B
Pilning HABD	16B
PINHOE	17C
Pinhoe LC (AHBC)	17C
PINNER (LU)	18D
Pirton LC (AHBC)	15B
Plasser UK Works	2A
Plassers LC (AOCL)	2A
PLYM VALLEY RAILWAY	8A
PLYMOUTH	8B
Plymouth East GF	8B
Plymouth Friary (DBS)	8A
Plymouth Laira Depot	8A
PLYMOUTH ROAD (BTR)	30B
Plymouth SC (P)	8B
(Plympton)	8A
Poden Farm LC (UWC)	13D
Polperro Tunnel	10A
POLSLOE BRIDGE	18B
Ponsanooth (New) Viaduct	10A
Ponsondane LC (UWC)	10B
Ponsondane Loading Banks (DBS)	10B
PONT GOCH (TVR)	32D
(Pont Lliw)	25A
Pontamman Tunnel	31C
PONTARDDULAIS	25A, 31D
Pontarddulais Tunnel	25A, 31D
Ponthir LC (UWC)	27D
PONTLOTTYN	28B
Pontlottyn Viaduct	28B
PONTPRENSHITW (TVR)	32D
Pontprenshitw Viaduct (TVR)	32D
Pontrilas SB (PS)	27C
Pontrilas Tunnel	27C
Pontsarn HABD	23A
Pontsarn LC (AHBC)	23A
Pontsmill Viaduct	9B
PONTSTICILL (BMR)	32J
Pontyates LC (TMO)	25B
Pontyberem LC (TMO)	25B
PONTYCLUN	23A
Pontycymmer (Ffaldau)	29B
Pontyfelir LC (RGR)	32L
PONTYPOOL & NEW INN	27D
PONTYPOOL AND BLAENAVON RAILWAY	32K
PONTYPRIDD	29A
Pontypridd North Jn	29A
Pontypridd South Jn	29A
Poole's LC (UWC)	20A
Pools LC (UWC)	13D
(Poplar Jn) Acton East Jn	1B
Port Talbot Docks (ABP)	23C
Port Talbot East (Taibach)	23C
Port Talbot HABD	23C
PORT TALBOT PARKWAY	23C
Port Talbot Parkway LC (MCB)	23C
Port Talbot SC (PT)	23C
Port Talbot West HABD	23C
Port Walleroo LC	24A
PORTBURY	5B
Portbury Dock Jn	5B
Portbury Terminal Jn	17A
PORTH	29A
Porthkerry Tunnel No.1	30A
Porthkerry Tunnels No.2	30A
Porthkerry Viaduct	30A
PORTISHEAD	5B
Portobello Jn	1A
(Portskewett)	20B
PORTSMOUTH ARMS	10C
Portsmouth Arms No.1 LC (UWC)	10C
Portsmouth Arms No.1 LC (UWC)	10C
Post Office No.1 LC (TMO) (Sudbrook)	20B
Post Office No.2 LC (TM) (Sudbrook)	20B
Pound Lane LC (UWC)	18A
Poundbury Viaduct	18A
Powderham Crossing LC	7B
Powell LC (UWC)	27C
PRESTON ROAD (LU)	18D
Price Church Farm LC (UWC)	27C
Prideaux Viaduct	9B
PRINCE STREET (BIM)	32H
PRINCES RISBOROUGH	19B
Princes Risborough Jns	19B
Probotec Maintenance Depot	12A
(Probus)	10A
Pulp Mills LC (TMO) (Sudbrook)	20B
Purton Collins Lane LC (AHBC)	15A
Purton Common LC	15A
(Purton)	15A
Puxton & Worle LC (MCB)	6A
PYLE	23B
Pylie Hill	5B
Pylie Hill GF	5B
QUAINTON ROAD	18E
QUAINTON ROAD (BRC)	32B
Quainton Road Jn	18E
Quainton Road SB (BRC)	32B
QUAKER'S YARD	29A
Quaker's Yard Viaduct	29A
Quay Loop GF (BIM)	32H
(Quedgley)	16A
Queen Street North Jn	28B
Queen Street South Jn	22, 28B
Queens Park GF (DSR)	7C
QUINTRELL DOWNS	9C
Quintrell Downs Station LC (ABCL)	9C
Rabber Farm LC (UWC)	31A
Racecourse Sidings (Newbury)	11A
RADLEY	12C
Radley HABD	12C
(Radstock)	12A
RADYR	28B
Radyr Branch Jn	22
Radyr Jn	28B
Radyr Jn SC (VR)	28B
Radyr North Jn	28B
Raikes LC (UWC)	31B
Rail Recycling Centre (Thingley Jn)	4C
(Rainbow Hill Jn)	14A
Rainbow Hill Tunnel	14A
Rattery Bank	7C
Rattery Viaduct	7C
Raven LC (AOCL)	31
READING	3A, 3
Reading Depot (FGW)	3
Reading New Jn	3A, 3
Reading Old Jn	3
Reading SC (R)	3A,3
Reading Southern Jn (2011)	3
Reading Spur Jn	3A, 3
Reading Triangle Sidings	3
READING WEST	3A, 11
Reading West Jn Up Yard	3
Read's G F	28
Red Cow LC (CCTV)	7
Red Hill Jn	27
Red Hill Tunnel	27
REDLAND	17
REDRUTH	10
Redruth Tunnel	10
Redruth Viaduct	10
Refuse Transfer Station (Westerleigh)	16
Regents Canal Viaduct	18
(Reso!ven)	24
REWLEY ROAD (BRC)	32
RHEILFFORDD GWILI RAILWAY	32
RHIWBINA	28
Rhiwderin LC (AOCL)	28
Rhondda Viaduct	29
RHOOSE	30
Rhoose LC (CCTV)	30
Rhosferig Tunnel	31
Rhubarb Loop	5
Rhydilyn LC (UWC)	31
Rhyd-y-Fynnon Farm LC (UWC)	31
RHYMNEY	28
Rhymney Sidings South GF	28
Rhymney Valley	28
Richard's LC (UWC)	7
RICKMANSWORTH (LU)	18
Rickmansworth North Sidings	18
Rickmansworth South Sidings	18
Rimmel's LC (UWC)	14
Rinse Apron (Maliphant)	24
RISCA & PONTYMISTER	28
Risca South Jn	28
River Avon Underbridge (Bristol)	5
River Avon Viaduct (AVR)	32
River Avon Viaduct (Chippenham)	4
River Avon Viaduct (Defford)	15
River Avon Viaduct (Evesham)	13
River Boyd Viaduct (AVR)	32
River Brent Viaduct	19
River Clyst Viaduct	18
River Colne Viaduct	19
River Dart Viaduct	7
River Ely Viaduct	23
River Exe Viaduct (Exeter St. Davids)	7
River Frome Viaduct	18
River Gade Viaduct (LU)	18
River Isis Bridge (Oxford)	12
River Lodden Viaduct	3
River Neath Viaduct	24
River Otter Viaduct	17
River Plym Viaduct	8
River Ray Viaduct (S&CR)	32
River Tavy Viaduct	8
River Tawe Viaduct	25
River Teign Sea Walls	7
River Teign Viaduct	7
River Teme Viaduct (Worcester)	14
River Thame Viaduct	19
River Towy Viaduct	31
River Usk Viaduct	21
River Wye Viaduct	31
Riverside Freight Yard (Exeter)	7
Riverside Siding (Cardiff)	2
(Roath Branch Jn)	28
Robertstown LC (TMO)	29
Robeston Refinery (Milford Haven)	26
ROCHE	9
Rock Dries Siding (Imerys)	9
Rockingham Road	17
Rockmill Viaduct	9
Roebuck Gate LC (AOCL) (WSR)	6
ROGERSTONE	28
Rose Farm LC (UWC)	19
Roskear Jn LC (MCB)	10
Roskear Jn SB (R)	10
Rotherwas Jn	27
(Roundball)	17
Roundham LC (R/G-X)	13
RADYR	
Royal Albert Bridge	8
Royal Edward Yard	17
ROYAL OAK (LU)	1
Royal Oak Sidings	1
Royal Portbury Dock	5
Ruddle Lake LC (UWC)	20
Ruislip Depot (LU)	19
RUISLIP GARDENS (LU)	19
Rumney River Bridge	21
Rumney River Bridge Jn	21
(Ruscombe)	20

Location	Code
TENBY	26C
Tenby (Greenhill) Viaduct	26C
Tenby GF	26C
Terras LC (Open)	9A
Tesco Covered Way	19B
Thame Jn (C&PRR)	19B
Thames Valley SC (TVCC)	3C
THATCHAM	11A
The Farm LC (UWC)	26B
The Feeder	5B
The Grove LC (UWC)	27C
The Hall Farm No.3 LC (UWC)	31A
THEALE	11A
Theale GSP	11A
Theale Sidings	11A
Thingley Jn	4C
Thomas LC (UWC)	27C
Thomas No.1 LC (UWC)	31A
Thomas No.2 LC (UWC)	31A
Thorney Marsh Lane LC (UWC)	17B
Thorney Mill Sidings	2B
THORNFORD	18A
Thornford Bridge LC (UWC)	18A
Three Gates LC (UWC)	20B
Tidal Sidings (DBS)	21B
Tidal Sidings GF (Cardiff)	21B
Tidal Yard LC	21B
Tidenham	20B
TILEHURST	3C
Tilehurst East Jn	3C
Tir-Allen Farm No.1 LC (UWC)	31C
Tir-Allen Farm No.2 LC (UWC)	31C
Tirclau LC (Open)	25B
Tirlsaf No.1 LC (UWC)	24B
TIR-PHIL	28B
Tirydail LC (ABCL)	31C
(Tiverton Junction)	7A
Tiverton Loops	7A
TIVERTON PARKWAY	6D
TODDINGTON (GWR)	32A
Toddington SB (GWR)	32A
TON PENTRE	29A
TONDU	29B
Tondu Jn	29B
Tondu SB	29B
TONYPANDY	29A
TOPSHAM	18B
Topsham LC (CCTV)	18B
Torcoed No.2 LC	23A
TORQUAY	7C
Torr Works Quarry	12A
TORRE	7C
Total Sidings GF	2B
Total/Fina Oil (Colnbrook)	2B
TOTNES	7C
Totnes East	7C
TOTNES LITTLEHEMPSTON (SDR)	7C
Towan LC (UWC)	10B
Tower Colliery	29A
Towney LC (UWC)	11A
Tram Inn LC (MCB)	27C
Tram Inn SB (TI)	27C
Trecwn Branch	26B
Trecwn Jn	26B
Tredington LC (AHBC)	15D
TREDOMEN	28B
Tredomen	28B
Treffoliad Farm LC (UWC)	31B
TREFOREST	29A
TREFOREST ESTATE	29A
Tregagle Viaduct	10A
Tregarne Viaduct	10A
Tregoss Moor LC (AOCL)	9C
TREHAFOD	29A
TREHERBERT	29A
Treherbert GF	29A
Trelavour Siding (Goonwean Ltd)	9C
(Trelewis)	28B
Tremains Loop	23A
Tremorfa Works (CELSA)	21B
Tremorfa Works GF	21B
Trenance Viaduct	9C
Trencreek LC (AOCL)	9C
Trenowin (Lower) LC (UWC)	10B
Trenowin Upper LC (UWC)	10B
TREORCHY	29A
Tresithney No.2 LC (UWC)	9C
Tresulgan Viaduct	9A
Treverrin HABD	9B
Treverrin Tunnel	9B
Treviddo Viaduct	9A
Treviscoe Siding (Imerys)	9C
Trewern Farm LC (UWC)	26A
Trewern Mill LC (UWC)	26A
TROED-Y-RHIW	29A
Troed-y-Rhiw Fedwen LC (UWC)	31A
Trostre Works (Corus)	25A
Trostre Works Jn	25A
TROWBRIDGE	11C
(Trumpers Crossing)	2A
(Trunk Siding Jn)	26B
TRURO	10A
Truro Freight Sidings (DBS)	10A
Truro SB (T)	10A
Truro Station LC (MCB)	10A
Truro Viaduct	10A
Tucker's LC (UWC)	4C
Tuckwells LC	12C
Tuffley	16A
Tufts Jn (DFR)	20D
Turf Lock LC (UWC)	7B
Turnchapel Branch Jn	8A
Tutshill (or Chepstow) Tunnel	20B
Twerton HABD	4C
Twerton Long Tunnel	4C
Twerton Short Tunnel	4C
Twerton Viaduct	4C
TWYFORD	3A
Twyford East	3A
Twyford HABD	3A
Twyford West	3A
TY GLAS	28B
Ty-Ddu LC (UWC)	31A
Tynewydd No.2 LC (UWC)	26A
Tynycerig No.1 LC (UWC)	31D
Tynycerig No.2 LC (UWC)	31D
Tynycerig No.3 LC (UWC)	31D
Tyn-y-Cynilwyn LC (UWC)	31D
Tyn-y-Maes LC (UWC)	31B
Tytherington	16B
Tytherington Tunnel	16B
Ty-Uchaf LC (AOCL)	31C
Uffington	4A
Ufton Goods Loop	11A
Ufton LC (AHBC)	11A
UMBERLEIGH	10C
Umberleigh Barton No.3 LC (UWC)	10C
Umberleigh LC (AOCL)	10C
Umberleigh River Viaduct	10C
(Undy)	20C
Up Flying Loop Jn	24A
Up Sidings GF (Reading)	3A
Uphill Jn	6A
Upper Cellws LC (UWC)	31B
Upper Chapel Hill Farm LC (UWC)	26C
(Upton Scudamore)	11C
Urchfont HABD	11C
Uskmouth	21A
(Uxbridge Branch Jn)	2B
Valley Farm LC (UWS)	19C
Varteg Road Viaduct (P&BR)	32K
Vastern Road Bridge	3A, 3D
VERNEY JN	13A
Victoria Road Stabling Sidings (St. Philips Marsh)	5B
Victory LC (AHBC)	6D
Vineyard Farm No.2 LC (UWC)	27C
Wadborough LC (AHBC)	15B
Wain Hill LC (C&PRR)	19B
WAINHILL HALT (C&PRR)	19B
Walden's LC	11C
Walker Lines (B&WR)	9A
WALLINGFORD (C&WR)	32G
Wallingford By-pass LC (ABCL) (C&WR)	32G
Waltham WILD	2C
Wansdyke LC (UWC)	11B
(Wanstrow)	12A
Wantage Road	4A
WANTAGE ROAD	4A
Wantage Road HABD	4A
(Wapley Common)	14C
Wapping Wharf Jn (BIM)	32H
WARGRAVE	3A
WARMINSTER	11C
Warminster HABD	11C
Warminster Incline	11C
WASHFORD (WSR)	6C
Waste Recycling Group (Calvert)	13A
WATCHET (WSR)	6C
Water Eaton LC (UWC)	13A
Water Lane LC (UWC)	18B
(Water Street Jn)	23B
WATERFRONT (BTR)	30B
Waterhead Viaduct (DSR)	7C
Waterloo Loop Jn	21A
Waterston (Milford Haven)	26B
Waterton (Bridgend)	23A
Waterton LC (AOCL)	23A
Waterworks LC (Open) (SDR)	7C
Watford East Jn	18D
Watford North Jn	18D
Watford South Jn	18D
Watson LC (UWC)	13D
Watts Blake Bearne Siding	7C
Watts Viaduct	15A
WAUN-GRON PARK	23A
Weighbridge GF (Bridgwater)	6B
Weirmarsh Viaduct	10C
Wellington HABD	27B
Wellington LC (AHBC)	27B
(Wellington)	6D
Wembley Depot (Chiltern Railways)	19
WEMBLEY PARK (LU)	18
WEMBLEY STADIUM	19
WENDOVER	18
Wentloog East Jn	21
Wentloog Freight Terminal (Freightliner)	21
Wentloog West Jn	21
WEST DRAYTON	2
West Drayton (Hanson)	2
West Drayton East	2
West Drayton Jn	2
WEST EALING	2
West Ealing Jn	2
WEST HAMPSTEAD (LU)	18
West Largin Viaduct	9
West London Refuse Transfer Station	2
West Midlands Sidings	12
WEST RUISLIP	19
WEST SOMERSET RAILWAY	6C, 6
West Wharf (Avonmouth)	17
(West Wycombe)	19
WESTBOURNE PARK (LU)	1
WESTBURY	11
Westbury Down Sidings	11
Westbury East Loop Jn	11
Westbury LC (AHBC)	20
Westbury Line Jn	3
Westbury Line Jn (Reading)	3
Westbury North Jn	11
Westbury SC (W)	11
Westbury South Jn	11
Westbury Track Recycling Centre	11
Westerleigh Freight Terminal	16
Westerleigh Jn	14C, 16
Westerleigh LC (UWC)	16
Western Growers LC	10
Westford (Cutlers) LC	6
Westford Foot LC (UWC)	17
Westinghouse Siding	2
Weston Mill Viaduct	8
WESTON MILTON	6
WESTON-SUPER-MARE	6
Weston-Super-Mare Up GF	6
Wests Bridge Farm LC (UWC)	27
Westway Overbridge	1
Westwood Viaduct	9
Wharncliffe Viaduct	2
Whatley Quarry	12
WHIMPLE	17
WHISTLE INN (P&BR)	32
WHITCHURCH	28
White House Mill LC (UWC)	26
Whiteball Summit	6
Whiteball Tunnel	6
(Whitecroft) (DFR)	20
Whitehouse Tunnel	19
White's Crossing LC	12
White's Crossing Siding	12
Whites Farm LC (UWC)	15
Whites LC (UWC)	13
WHITLAND	26
Whitland Down Sidings GF	26
Whitland Jn	26
Whitland SB (W)	26
Whitland Station LC (MCB)	26
Whitland Tunnel	26
Whitterleys Farm LC (UWC)	31
Wickham Knights LC (UWC)	11
Wickwar Tunnel	16
Wilderness LC	17
WILDMILL	29
WILLESDEN GREEN (LU)	18
WILLITON (WSR)	6
Williton GF (WSR)	6
Willow Vale Viaduct	12
Willox Bridge No.1 LC (UWC)	27
Wimborne Road LC	30
WINCHCOMBE (GWR)	32
WINDSOR & ETON CENTRAL	2
Windsor Branch Jn	2
Windsor Road Overbridge	2
Windsor Viaducts	2
Winsel Crossing LC (UWC)	26
WINSLOW	13
Winterbourne Viaduct	16
(Winterbourne)	16
(Witham)	12
(Withington)	14
Wivelscombe Tunnel	9
Wolvercot Tunnel	13
Wolvercot Jn	13
Woodborough Loops	11
Woodborough Sidings GF	11
WOODHAM HALT (BTR)	30
Woodlands LC (UWC)	26
Woofferton Jn	27
Woolaston LC (R/G)	20
Wooliams No.1 LC (UWC)	13
Wooliams No.2 LC (UWC)	13
Wooliams No.3 LC (UWC)	13
Wootton Basset GF	4

Index of Engineers Line References

This listing is intended to show all the relevant operational ELRs, those that were live in the last edition but now closed, out of use or lifted and those that have carried over from the original network onto Heritage lines. The location of the start and finish boundary of each ELR is indicated by the page references, usually low mileage first. Where both boundaries appear on the same page, only one reference is given. Some ELRs extend over several pages but due to space considerations, the intermediate page references have not been given.

Index of Lines of Route

Lines on the Network are nowadays given a Line of Route code (LOR) which may run over a number of ELRs. LORs have their origin in the codes used in the early 1990's in BR's Western Region. These were extended nationally by Railtrack in the late 90's and have links with the Possession Resource Information Database (PRIDE) codes. More information can be found about these codes on the excellent website by Phil Deaves at http://deaves47.users.btopenworld.com/rail_index.htm. The location of the start and finish of each Line of Route in is indicated by the page references below, usually low mileage first. The description against each code is the one generally used within the industry but the order of individual names within the description does not necessarily follow rising mileage. As severa ELR's can be covered by one LOR, mileages within itcan rise and fall.